SCIENCE

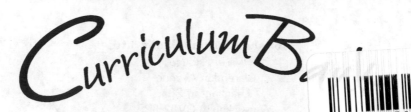

Curriculum B...

KEY STAGE ONE
SCOTTISH LEVELS A-B

SCIENCE

BRIAN PENGELLY AND GEORGINA BEASLEY

Published by Scholastic Ltd,
Villiers House,
Clarendon Avenue,
Leamington Spa,
Warwickshire CV32 5PR
Text © Brian Pengelly and Georgina Beasley
© 1995 Scholastic Ltd
67890   89012345

AUTHORS
BRIAN PENGELLY AND GEORGINA BEASLEY

EDITOR
IRENE GOODACRE

SERIES DESIGNER
LYNNE JOESBURY

DESIGNER
CLARE BREWER

ILLUSTRATIONS
MICK REID

COVER ILLUSTRATION
GAY STURROCK

INFORMATION TECHNOLOGY CONSULTANT
MARTIN BLOWS

SCOTTISH 5–14 LINKS
MARGARET SCOTT AND SUSAN GOW

Designed using Aldus Pagemaker

British Library Cataloguing-in-Publication Data
A catalogue record for this book is available from the
British Library.

ISBN 0-590-53387-8

Contents

ACKNOWLEDGEMENTS

This book was written with support from the Hertfordshire Science Teaching Scholarship, a trust funded jointly by John Murray (Publishers) Ltd and DG Mackean, and administered by Hertfordshire LEA.

The authors wish to acknowledge the generous assistance provided by the Hertfordshire Science Teaching Scholarship and the support of colleagues and children at Cropthorne with Charlton CE First School and Moon's Moat First and Nursery School.

Introduction

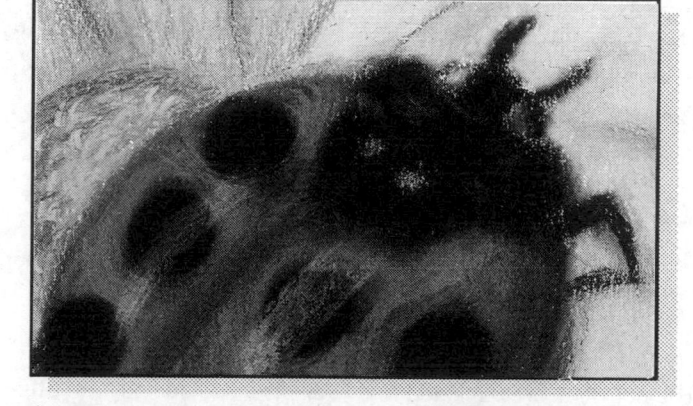

Scholastic Curriculum Bank is a series for all primary teachers, providing both an essential planning tool for devising comprehensive schemes of work as well as an easily accessible and varied bank of practical, classroom-tested activities with photocopiable resources.

Designed to help planning for and implementation of progression, differentiation and assessment, *Scholastic Curriculum Bank* offers a structured range of stimulating activities with clearly-stated learning objectives that reflect the programmes of study, and detailed lesson plans that allow busy teachers to put the ideas into practice with the minimum amount of preparation time. The photocopiable sheets that accompany many of the activities provide ways of integrating purposeful application of knowledge and skills, differentiation, assessment and record-keeping.

Opportunities for formative assessment are highlighted where appropriate within the activities, while separate summative assessment activities give guidelines for analysis and subsequent action. Ways of using information technology for different purposes and within different contexts, as a tool for communicating and handling information and as a method for investigating, are integrated into the activities where appropriate and more explicit guidance is provided at the end of the book.

The series covers all the primary curriculum subjects with separate books for Key Stages 1 and 2/Scottish levels A – B and C – E. It can be used as a flexible resource with any scheme to fulfil National Curriculum and Scottish 5–14 requirements and to provide children with a variety of different learning experiences that will lead to effective acquisition of skills and knowledge.

SCHOLASTIC CURRICULUM BANK SCIENCE

The *Scholastic Curriculum Bank Science* books enable teachers to plan comprehensive and structured coverage of the primary science curriculum and pupils to develop the required skills, knowledge and understanding through activities that promote scientific thinking and ways of working.

Each book covers one key stage. At Key Stage 1/Levels A – B all areas of science are covered, while at Key Stage 2/Levels C – E there are three books which reflect the sections of the Programme of Study (Life Processes and Living Things, Materials and their Properties, and Physical Processes). Experimental and investigative science is integrated into the three Key Stage 2/Scottish levels C-E books so that it is tackled in context.

Bank of activities

This book provides a bank of activities that can be used in many different ways to form a framework for a scheme of work; to add breadth and variety to an existing scheme; to supplement a particular topic. The activities are designed to address a number of important areas of study.

Systematic enquiry

A wide range of activities have been presented to enable opportunities for focused exploration and investigation to acquire scientific knowledge, understanding and skills. The activities involve both first-hand experience and the use of other sources of information. Opportunities for the use of IT for storing, retrieving and presenting information, and for investigative purposes are suggested throughout.

Communication skills

The activities aim to develop children's communication skills by encouraging pupils to:
▲ ask questions;
▲ use standard measures;

▲ discuss findings with others;
▲ present data in a variety of different ways.

Science in everyday life

Through a variety of domestic and environmental contexts, pupils are able to acquire an awareness of the importance of science in everyday life, of the part science has played in the development of many of the things they use and of treating their environment with care and sensitivity.

The nature of scientific ideas

The activities will help children to understand that scientific knowledge and understanding rely on evidence and that scientific evidence can be obtained in a number of ways. They also help the children to realise that science can provide explanations for many of the things that happen around them.

Health and safety

The activities encourage children to develop their knowledge and understanding of health and safety when working with living things and with materials. They will help pupils to recognise hazards to themselves and others, assess the risks to themselves and others, and take action to help control the risks.

Lesson plans

Detailed lesson plans, under clear headings, are given for each activity and provide teacher-ready material for immediate implementation in the classroom. Each lesson can be used as a starting point for further science. Teachers of Reception classes may choose to spread the material contained within each learning objective over a number of separate lessons.

SCIENCE

Activity title box

The information contained in the box at the beginning of each activity outlines the following key aspects:

▲ *Activity title and learning objective:* For each activity a clearly stated learning objective is given in bold italics. These present aspects of the programme of study in manageable, hierarchical teaching and learning chunks, and their purpose is to aid planning for progression. These objectives can be easily referenced to the National Curriculum and Scottish 5 – 14 requirements by using the overview grids on pages 9 to 12.

▲ *Class organisation/Likely duration:* Icons (†† and ⏲) signpost the suggested group sizes for each activity and the approximate amount of time required.

Safety: Where necessary, safety considerations are flagged with the ⚠ icon.

Previous skills/knowledge needed

Information is given here when it is necessary for the children to have acquired specific knowledge or skills prior to carrying out the activity.

Key background information

Most teachers of Key Stage 1 children will have all the necessary scientific knowledge to teach the lessons included in this book. On the few occasions where additional guidance may be helpful it is included under this heading.

Preparation

Advice is given for those occasions where it is necessary for the teacher to prime the pupils for the activity, prepare materials, or set up a display or activity ahead of time.

Resources needed

All of the materials needed to carry out the activity are listed so that the teacher can gather them together before the beginning of the teaching session.

Language to be introduced

A list of words is provided for inclusion in language development work. The words can be used before, during and after the lessons to help pupils communicate their understanding more clearly.

What to do

Easy to follow, step-by-step instructions are given for carrying out the activity including, where appropriate, suggested questions for the teacher to ask the pupils to help instigate discussion and stimulate investigation.

Suggestion(s) for extension/support

Where the activities lend themselves to it ideas are given for ways of providing for easy differentiation. Suggestions are provided as to how each activity can be modified for the less able or extended for the more able.

Assessment opportunities

Where appropriate, opportunities for ongoing assessment, during or after a specific activity, are highlighted. Teachers may also use the open-ended questions contained in each lesson to encourage the children to show what they know and understand.

Opportunities for IT

Where opportunities for IT present themselves these are briefly outlined with reference to suitable types of program. The chart on page 160 presents specific areas of IT covered in the activities, together with more detailed support on how to apply particular types of program.

Display ideas

Where relevant and innovative, display ideas are incorporated into activity plans and illustrated with examples.

Other aspects of the Science PoS covered

Inevitably, activities will cover aspects of the programmes of study in other areas of the science curriculum and, in particular, Experimental and Investigative Science will be a feature of many of them. These links are highlighted under this heading.

Reference to photocopiable sheets

Where activities include photocopiable activity sheets, small reproductions of these are included in the lesson plans together with notes on how they should be used.

Investigations

Although aspects of Experimental and Investigative Science will be integral to most activities, each book includes a separate section of investigations and real-life problem-solving activities. These are more open-ended than the rest of the activities and provide opportunities to test ideas and carry out whole investigations, utilising and building on their content knowledge. Guidance for the teacher on concepts likely to emerge from such investigations is given. Activities suitable for investigations are flagged by the 🔍 icon.

Assessment

This chapter provides a range of tasks related to the main areas of study covered elsewhere in the book that can be used for summative assessment purposes. The activities have been designed so that they can be used either as individual tasks to provide the teacher with ongoing evaluation of children's progress or, alternatively, to be presented together as a form of summative assessment at the end of a whole unit or at the end of Key Stage 1. The worksheets that accompany these assessment tasks are included in the photocopiable section on pages 113 to 157. Activities intended for assessment purposes are flagged by the ✍ icon.

Photocopiable activity sheets

Many of the activities are accompanied by photocopiable activity sheets. For some activities, there may be more than one version, or an activity sheet will be 'generic' with a facility for the teacher to fill in the appropriate task in order to provide differentiation by task. Other sheets may be more open-ended to provide differentiation by outcome. The photocopiable activity sheets provide purposeful activities that are ideal for assessment and can be kept as records in pupils' portfolios of work.

Cross-curricular links

Cross-curricular links are identified on a simple grid cross-referencing the particular areas of study in science to the programme of study for other subjects in the curriculum, and where appropriate provides suggestions for activities. See page 160.

Overview grid

The overview grid on pages 9 to 12 provides an invaluable planning tool which can be used in a number of ways:
▲ to select learning objectives that are relevant to your class;
▲ to plan a programme of work;
▲ to map activities in this book directly to the Science PoS for Key Stage 1 or the Scottish 5-14 requirements;
▲ to help easy lesson planning by providing at-a-glance guidance on class organisation and lesson content.

SCIENCE AT KEY STAGE 1

Science at Key Stage 1 involves learning by doing. This means that when there is science going on it is likely to be accompanied by noise, mess and movement. The activities in this book have been designed to help you manage the noise, mess and movement so that science becomes an enjoyable and rewarding part of the curriculum for teachers and pupils.

On occasion, you will find it easier to organise your class so that groups of children take turns at the science activity. Many of the lessons can be organised as whole-class lessons and most will be enhanced if the ideas to be explored are introduced to the whole class at discussion time.

In a busy classroom no Key Stage 1 teacher can sit exclusively with one group of children and ignore the rest of the class, but teachers should remember that children need to be listened to and helped individually in science in the same way that they are taught how to read. There is a strong case for using additional adults to facilitate the teaching of science, but these additional adults should not be relied on to tackle the highly demanding job of teaching science unless they are qualified to do so.

Teaching science at Key Stage 1 is not a matter of telling the children what they should know. On the contrary, trying to help children develop scientific concepts by telling them a series of facts will, most likely, leave them in a state of confusion. The art of teaching science is to listen to your pupils and respond to them, drawing from them what they know. Give them the language to express their understanding and plan activities which will help them develop their knowledge and understanding further.

The most useful teaching and assessment strategy is that of asking open-ended questions. You can use the questions provided in each lesson to help the children identify what is relevant to each situation they encounter and help them raise questions of their own. If children can identify what is relevant and ask questions then they have the potential to become true scientists.

All the lessons contained in this book are tried and tested, but practical science does have the potential to be dangerous. Teachers should consult The ASE Safety Booklet *Be Safe* and check that they have fulfilled local safety requirements before attempting to teach any lesson which causes them concern.

Learning objective	PoS/AO	Content	Type of activity	Page
Life processes and living things				
We all have a sense of touch.	LP 2f *Processes of Life Level A*	Sorting a collection of objects with different feeling surfaces.	Group activity.	14
We use our sense of touch to be aware of the world around us.	LP 2f *Processes of Life Level A*	Investigating objects with different feeling surfaces.	Individual/paired activity.	15
We use our sense of sight to help us to be aware of the world around us.	LP 2f *Processes of Life Level A*	Sorting a collection of objects with different colours and patterns.	Paired activity.	16
We use our sense of hearing to listen to and recognise sounds.	LP 2f *Processes of Life Level A*	Identifying a collection of sounds.	Class/group activity.	18
We use our sense of taste to recognise flavours.	LP 2f *Processes of Life Level A*	Identifying flavours.	Individual within group activity.	18
We use our sense of smell to be aware of our world.	LP 2f *Processes of Life Level A*	Identifying smells.	Individual within group activity.	20
To recognise and name the parts of the body.	LP 2a *Variety and Characteristic Features Level A*	Naming and labelling the parts of the body.	Class or group activity.	21
We need to eat and drink to stay alive.	LP 2b *Processes of Life Level A*	Exploring what we eat and drink.	Individual within class activity.	22
Eating the right food is important to our health.	LP 2c *Looking after oneself Level A*	Exploring what we mean by healthy diet.	Group activity.	24
We need to exercise to keep healthy.	LP 2c *Looking after oneself Level A*	Investigating what happens to our bodies after exercise.	Class activity.	25
We sometimes need medicines or pills to make us well.	LP 2d *Looking after oneself Level A*	Discussing what happens when we are ill.	Class discussion. Individual research.	26
Humans have babies which grow into children and then adults.	LP 2e *Processes of Life Level A*	Inviting a mum or dad with a young baby to visit the class.	Class discussion.	27
We all grow.	LP 1b *Processes of Life Level A*	Collecting and comparing measurements.	Paired activity.	29
Some things about us are different. Some things about us are the same.	LP 4a *Variety and Characteristic Features Level A*	Investigating eye colour of pupils in the class.	Class or group activity.	30
Seeds have observable similarities and differences.	LP 4b *Variety and Characteristic Features Level A*	Sorting seeds according to size, colour, shape and pattern.	Small groups.	32

SCIENCE

Learning objective	PoS/AO	Content	Type of activity	Page
Seeds grow into plants.	LP 3c *Processes of Life Level A*	Planting seeds, observing and recording growth.	*Class introduction followed by group activity.*	33
Recognising and naming the parts of a flowering plant.	LP 3b *Variety and Characteristic Features Level A*	Naming parts of a flowering plant.	*Class or group activity.*	34
Plants need sunlight and water to grow.	LP 3a *Interaction of Living Things with their Environment Level B*	Investigating what happens to a plant when deprived of light.	*Class activity.*	35
Seeds grow into plants which produce seeds for their own kind.	LP 3c *Processes of Life Level B*	Competition to grow the tallest sunflower.	*Class activity.*	37
Different plants are found in the school environment.	LP 5a *Interaction of Living Things with their Environment Level B*	Making a survey of all the plants in the school environment.	*Class activity.*	39
Different animals are found in the school environment.	LP 5a *Interaction of Living Things with their Environment Level B*	Walking around the school environment to survey and record the animal life.	Class activity.	39
Different plants and animals are found in different environments.	LP 5b *Interaction of Living Things with their Environment Level B*	Visiting various environments and recording the plant and animal life.	Class or group activity.	41
Animals move, feed and grow.	LP 1b *Processes of Life Level B*	Observing the movements, feeding and growth of different snails.	Group investigation.	42
Some things have never been alive.	LP 1a *Materials from Earth Level A*	Making and sorting a collection of things that have never been alive.	Group activity. Individual recording.	44
People and animals have similarities and differences.	LP 4b *Variety and Characteristic Features Level A*	Sorting animals and people into groups according to observable similarities and differences.	Class introduction, followed by group activity.	45

Materials and their Properties

Learning objective	PoS/AO	Content	Type of activity	Page
We can use our senses to find similarities and differences between materials.	M 1a *Materials from Earth Level A*	Sorting a collection of materials which have different properties.	Class or group activity.	48
To be able to sort materials into groups according to properties of texture, appearance and transparency.	M 1b *Materials from Earth Level A*	Sorting a collection of materials which include transparent items.	Individual within group activity.	50
To know that some materials are magnetic and others are non-magnetic.	M 1b *Forces and their Effects Level B*	Investigating which materials are magnetic.	Group activity.	51

SCIENCE

Learning objective	PoS/AO	Content	Type of activity	Page
To be able to identify wood, textiles, plastic, rock, paper and metal.	M 1c *Materials from Earth Level A*	Sorting and naming a collection of common materials.	Class activity.	53
Some materials have many different uses.	M 1d *Materials from Earth Level A*	Making a survey of how wood, plastic, paper, rock, metal and textiles are used.	Group activity.	54
Some materials have specific uses.	M 1e *Materials from Earth Level A*	Investigating the properties of wood, plastic, paper, textiles and metal.	Group activity.	55
Some objects can have their shape changed by squashing.	M 2a *Materials from Earth Level A*	Making banana sandwiches.	Whole class, in groups.	57
Some objects can be changed in shape by bending.	M 2a *Materials from Earth Level A*	Making bendy puppets.	Individual activity.	59
Some objects can be changed in shape by twisting.	M 2a *Materials from Earth Level A*	Exploring a collection of threads.	Class or group activity.	60
Some objects can be changed in shape by stretching.	M 2a *Materials from Earth Level A*	Making sock puppets.	Class or group activity.	62
To describe the way in which water changes when it is cooled.	M 2b *On Planet Earth Level B*	Exploring the relationship between ice and water.	Small group activity.	63
To describe the way in which some materials change when they are heated or cooled.	M 2b *On Planet Earth Level B*	Making cakes with melted chocolate.	Small group activity.	65
Physical Processes				
Mains electricity is dangerous and can kill you.	PP 5a *Properties and Uses of Energy Level A*	Sorting electrical appliances into 'never touch', 'never touch the plug', 'safe to play with'.	Class discussion.	68
Many everyday appliances use electricity.	PP 1a *Properties and Uses of Energy Level A*	Considering a range of devices powered by electricity.	Class activity or groups in turn.	69
To learn how to make things work by constructing a simple circuit.	PP 1b *Properties and Uses of Energy Level B*	Making simple electrical circuits with batteries, bulbs and buzzers.	Individual activity within small groups.	71
A complete circuit is needed to make electrical things work.	PP 1c *Properties and Uses of Energy Level B*	Investigating wire and foil in circuits.	Individual activity within small groups.	72
To be able to describe the movement of familiar things.	PP 2a *Forces and their Effects Level A*	Exploring movement – pushes and pulls.	PE lesson followed by class discussion.	74
Pushes and pulls make things move.	PP 2b *Forces and their Effects Level A*	Investigating pushes and pulls with heavy objects.	Small-group practical then individual activity.	75

11

SCIENCE

Learning objective	PoS/AO	Content	Type of activity	Page
Forces can make things speed up, slow down or change direction.	PP 2c *Forces and their Effects Level A*	Investigating forces using balls, sand, water, sucking and blowing.	Individual or small group activity.	77
Forces can change the shape of objects.	PP 2d *Forces and their Effects Level A*	Exploring and investigating forces using malleable materials.	Individual work.	78
Light comes from a variety of sources.	PP 3a *Forms and Sources of Energy Level A*	Exploring a collection of shiny objects.	Individual activity within small groups.	79
Darkness is the absence of light.	PP 3b *Forms and Sources of Energy Level A*	Investigating shadows and light sources.	Group activity.	81
There are many kinds of sound.	PP 3c *Forms and Sources of Energy Level A*	Exploring a collection of instruments.	Class activity.	83
Different things make different sounds.	PP 3c *Forms and Sources of Energy Level B*	Identifying sources of sound.	Class activity.	85
Sound travels out from its source getting fainter as it goes.	PP 3d *Forms and Sources of Energy Level B*	Investigating the distance travelled by sound(s).	Class or group activity.	87
Investigations				
Physical Processes: Light	*	Can reflectors be seen in the dark?	Small group activity.	90
Physical Processes: Sound	*	How far away can you hear a sound?	Small group activity.	91
Life Processes and Living Things: Birds	*	Which foods do birds like best?	Class or group activity.	93
Life Processes and Living Things: Seeds	*	Do seeds need soil to grow?	Group activity.	95
Materials and their Properties: Absorbency	*	Which material is best for mopping up spills?	Group activity.	97
Materials and their Properties: Elasticity	*	Which material makes the best car launcher?	Small group activity.	99

* The investigations have not been linked to specific Programmes of Study or Attainment Outcomes to allow teachers flexibility to match the individual learning needs of the children in their class.

Life Processes & living things

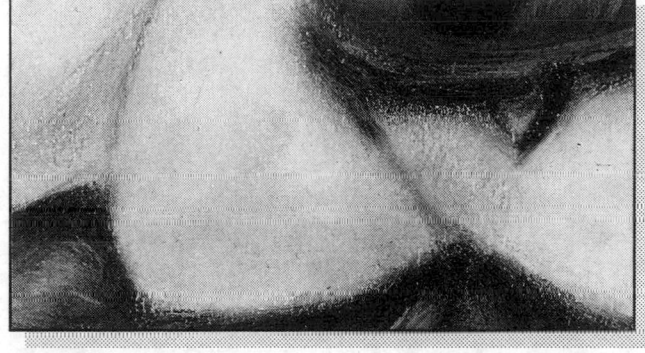

This section of the book contains activities on Life processes, Humans as organisms, Green plants as organisms, Variation and classification and Living things in their environment. Wherever possible first-hand experiences have been built into the lesson plans so that children can learn through practical experience. Where this has not been possible (in teaching about the role of drugs as medicine, for example) teachers will need to relate the activities to the experiences children bring with them from outside school. Sensitivity will be required in many of these lessons and teachers should try to include relevant aspects of health and safety teaching whenever possible.

Many of the activities can be enhanced by regular visits to a well-developed conservation area. You should consider creating a log pile or rock pile, or planting shrubs to attract birds and butterflies.

Encourage staff and pupils to contribute to the following collections of materials which can be stored with your science resources for use in numerous different sorting and classifying activities throughout the school:
▲ small metal objects;
▲ shiny/reflective surfaces;
▲ small objects with textured (interesting feeling) surfaces;
▲ transparent objects made from various materials.

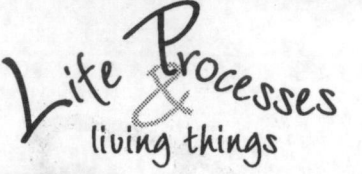

FEELING SURFACES

We all have a sense of touch.

†† *Whole-class lesson followed by children working in groups of six to eight.*

🕐 *40 minutes.*

⚠ *Be careful to choose objects which are safe to handle and will not cause injury.*

Previous skills/knowledge needed

Understanding of what is meant by texture. The collection of objects (see below) could be done as a previous activity.

Preparation

Make a fairly large collection of objects with surfaces which feel significantly different. Try to include a range of textures, including rough, smooth, fluffy, soft, cold, slippery, dry, hard, bumpy, and so on. (Consider using cotton wool, a spoon, a pencil, a Sticklebrick, LEGO, sandpaper, a stone, an apple, ice cubes, a ball of wool, marbles.)

Resources needed

Copies of the photocopiable sheets on pages 114, 115 and 116 (as required), a collection of objects for feeling, sorting rings, blank labels, felt-tipped pens, a large floor or table area.

Language to be introduced

Texture, touch, feel, rough, smooth, cold, fluffy, slippery, soft, dry, hard, bumpy, sharp, spiky, rigid, bendy, squashy, tickly, lumpy, bristly, blunt.

What to do

Gather the children into a circle. Place the collection of objects in the centre and ask the children to select one object. Pass the object round the circle so that everyone has a chance to feel it. Ask each child to tell you one thing about what the object feels like. Explain that they are describing its texture. Ask the children which part of the body they use to feel with. Place the object in a sorting ring. Encourage each child to find another object which has the same texture and can therefore be placed in the same ring. Then ask if anyone can think of a word to label the set.

Choose another object and repeat the exercise.

Ask the children if they can use their sense of touch to make another set from the remaining objects, using a different word to describe it. Can anyone think of a describing word and find objects to match it?

Some objects may fit into two sets. In this case either let the children decide which set the item should go in, or find a similar object so that you have one for each set. Finally, ask the children how they want to record what they have done.

The photocopiable sheet on page 114 can be used to record the children's ideas. Children should be encouraged to think of their own describing words for the labels and praised if they choose appropriate words. The information can also be recorded using Carroll diagrams (photocopiable page 116). This activity can be repeated as group work during the week, allowing the children to contribute to an interactive display.

Suggestion(s) for extension

Find some objects which could belong to one or more sets and add these to your collection. Introduce the more able children to the idea of overlapping sets. The photocopiable sheet on page 115 will help you to record this. Make a note of the children who can sort using this new concept.

Suggestion(s) for support

Some children will not have the language development necessary to explain how they want to sort the objects. By watching the children's reactions closely during the activity, you can assess which children have thought of a way and invite them to show you by physically moving the groupings. They can then be introduced to the appropriate language and encouraged to describe what they have done.

Assessment opportunities

As they work, look out for pupils who are able to sort a group of objects according to what they feel like.

▲ Which children understand the concept of a 'set'?

▲ Who can select objects appropriate to the set?

▲ Do any children suggest other categories for sorting?

Watch the pupils to see who is able to visualise a set.

Display ideas

Make an interactive display of the collection of objects on a cupboard or table-top. Include labels of groupings, key questions and blank labels for the children to add their own ideas. Display the children's recordings on a board above.

Other aspects of the Science PoS covered

Experimental and Investigative Science – 2a.
Materials and their Properties – 1a, 1b, 1c.

Reference to photocopiable sheets

Page 114 is a differentiated simple Venn diagram in which the children can draw their collected objects sorted according to their own chosen criteria. You may wish the children to divide their set into subsets by writing, for example, 'these objects are all rough but some of them are also rigid'.

Page 115 is an extension of the simple Venn diagram. The children are asked to sort their objects into two sets, using two separate criteria, with some objects belonging to both sets. Only the more able will be able to attempt this exercise.

Page 116 is an example of a Carroll diagram. It is a recording strategy which requires the children to sort their selected objects according to two criteria and includes 'is' and 'is not' questioning. It is particularly appropriate for pupils who understand the subset/overlapping sets idea.

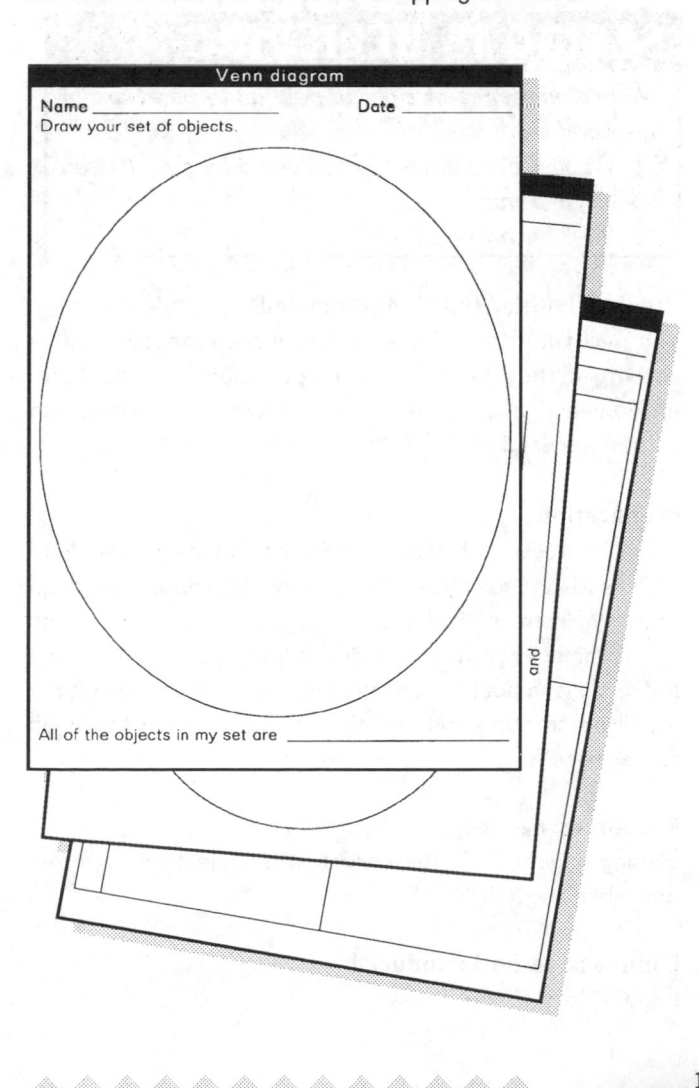

Venn diagram

Name _____ Date _____
Draw your set of objects.

and

All of the objects in my set are _____

FEELY BAGS

We use our sense of touch to be aware of the world around us.

†† *Whole class introduction followed by the children working individually or in pairs.*

⏱ *15–20 minutes.*

⚠ *Be careful to choose objects which are safe to handle and will not cause injury.*

Previous skills/knowledge needed

The children should have completed the lesson called 'Feeling surfaces' on page 14, or a similar sorting activity, in order to acquire the appropriate language.

Preparation

Select a few familiar objects with surfaces which feel significantly different. Put them into a feely bag or box. There should be enough bags for one between two children.

Resources needed

A number of feely bags (such as children's draw-string sports bags) or boxes.

Language to be introduced

Smooth, rough, hard, soft, curved, square, round, corners, cold, furry, long, pointed, sharp, prickly, texture.

What to do

Gather the group of children together. Talk to them about their sense of touch and ask them which part of the body they use to investigate the textures of new things. Tell them they are going to play a game called 'Find the object'. In this game they have to find an object, without looking, just by

using their sense of touch. Give one of the children a feely bag and ask her, without peeping, to put her hand inside the bag and choose one of the objects, without removing it from the bag. Ask her to describe to the rest of the children what it feels like:

▲ Does it feel smooth, rough, etc?
▲ How big is the object?
▲ Does it fit inside your hand?
▲ What shape is it?
▲ Is it round, curved, square, etc?
▲ Does it have corners?

Ask the listening group if they want to ask any questions about the mystery object. Finally, give the bag to one of the other children and ask him to find (still inside the bag) the object that has just been described. The child who chose the object originally should check by feeling whether it is the right one. If the correct object is not selected, keep passing the bag around until the right one is found. Repeat this exercise as many times as you feel necessary until the children fully understand the rules of the game.

Divide the children into pairs. Give each pair a feely bag and ask them to take it in turns to describe, then to find, an object. When all of the objects in the bag have been found, each pair should play the game with a different bag of objects. Monitor what the children are doing to make sure they are not making wild guesses and check that their descriptions match the chosen object.

Alternatively, prepare two feely bags, containing identical objects, so that the children can play 'Feeling Snap'. The rules of the game and content of the lesson are the same. When the finder is ready, both children should remove the objects from the bags at the same time to check that they have a matching pair (they could also shout 'Snap' if your nerves will stand it!).

Suggestion(s) for extension

Replace the objects with a number of different textured fabrics. Prepare a wall chart with a sample of each fabric displayed. Ask the children to choose a fabric on the wall chart, to feel it carefully and then to find the matching sample from the feely bag, using only their sense of touch.

Suggestion(s) for support

Some children may need help with the language required to describe the object. It may be better to let these children be the 'guessers' first in order to give them the opportunity to listen to the 'describers'.

Assessment opportunities

Make a note of the children who can and cannot use appropriate language to describe the object.

Make a note of the children who can apply the descriptions and use their sense of touch to find the object being described.

Display ideas

Make a textured wall, using rectangles of different textured fabrics and materials for the children to explore by touching. Descriptive words can be displayed around and on it. Hang the feely bags from the plastic cup hooks attached to the side or beneath the display so that the children can repeat the activity over a period of time.

Other aspects of the Science PoS covered

Experimental and Investigative Science – 2a, 3c.

SEEING IS BELIEVING

We use our sense of sight to help us to be aware of the world around us.

✝✝ *Whole-class introduction followed by the children working in pairs.*

🕐 *20–30 minutes.*

Previous skills/knowledge needed

You may find that the children are more receptive to this activity if they have already been out into the local environment to notice where and how colour, shape and pattern are used.

Preparation

Make a collection of pictures and photographs or models of objects which use pattern and/or colour to help identification or to give instructions. Include a picture or model of a police car, an ambulance, a fire engine, a post van, traffic lights, traffic signs, a post-box, a telephone box, a zebra crossing, a pelican crossing and commercial logos (often found on carrier bags).

Resources needed

Sorting rings, labels, the collection of objects or pictures described above.

Language to be introduced

Logo, colour, shape, pattern.

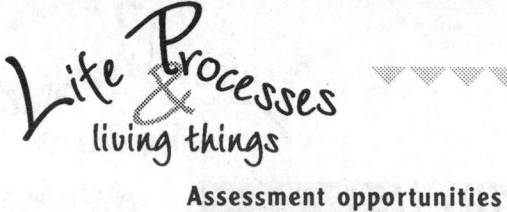

What to do

Talk to the children about their sense of sight. Ask them which part of the body they use to see with. Explain that they are going to use their sense of sight to sort the collection of objects or pictures.

Ask the children to sort the objects, pictures or photographs into sets of colours:
▲ Which colour is used most often?
▲ Which colours are not used at all?

Encourage them to think of a reason why some colours are used more often than others.

Next, ask the children to sort the objects, pictures or photographs into sets which use words, logos and pictures. The children will probably notice that firms and services use logos for identification. Explain that a logo is a special kind of picture.

Discuss why the children have chosen to put certain objects into particular sets. They could record and label the sets they have made using Venn diagrams (see pages 114 and 115) or Carroll diagrams (page 116).

Suggestion(s) for extension

Ask the children to sort the objects, pictures or photographs into sets with the following labels:
▲ These things use shape and/or colour to tell us what to do.
▲ These things use shape and/or colour to give us information.
▲ These things use shape and/or colour to tell us which company they belong to.
▲ These things are easy to see.

Ask questions to highlight the reasons why these shapes and colours are used:
▲ Why do we have traffic lights?
▲ What is the significance of the police car's flashing blue light?
▲ Why was blue chosen, and why does the light flash?
▲ Why do you think post vans are red?

Suggestion(s) for support

Be sensitive to the needs of the visually impaired child. An extra adult helper may be able to assess how well the child can see the resources being used, or you could try enlarging the pictures and photographs.

Assessment opportunities

Make a note of the children who can/cannot suggest why certain colours and patterns are used. Look out for reasoning such as:
▲ Post vans are all red so that we can identify them easily.
▲ Water hydrants are bright yellow for identification, and to make them easy to see from a distance.
▲ Traffic lights tell cars what to do.

These can then become hypotheses for further investigation.

Opportunities for IT

Children could use a simple word processor to write labels or sentences about the significance of the use of colour and pattern or they might use a simple art package to draw and experiment with different colours, even design a simple logo.

Display ideas

Make an interactive display of the sets the children make with the models, pictures and photographs.

Display the pictures and photographs with sentences made from the children's suggestions of the significance of the use of colour and pattern.

Other aspects of the Science PoS covered

Experimental and Investigative Science – 2a, 3a, 3c, 3d, 3f.

Reference to photocopiable sheets

Page 114 is a differentiated simple Venn diagram in which the children can draw the items in their sets sorted according to their own chosen criteria. Children could divide their set into subsets by writing, for example, 'these objects use red but some also use yellow'.

Page 115 is an extension of the simple Venn diagram, where children are asked to sort their objects into two sets, using two separate criteria, with some objects belonging to both sets. Only the more able will be able to attempt this exercise.

Page 116 is an example of a Carroll diagram. This recording strategy also asks pupils to sort their selected objects according to two criteria and involves 'is' and 'is not' questioning. It is particularly appropriate for pupils who understand the idea of subsets and overlapping sets.

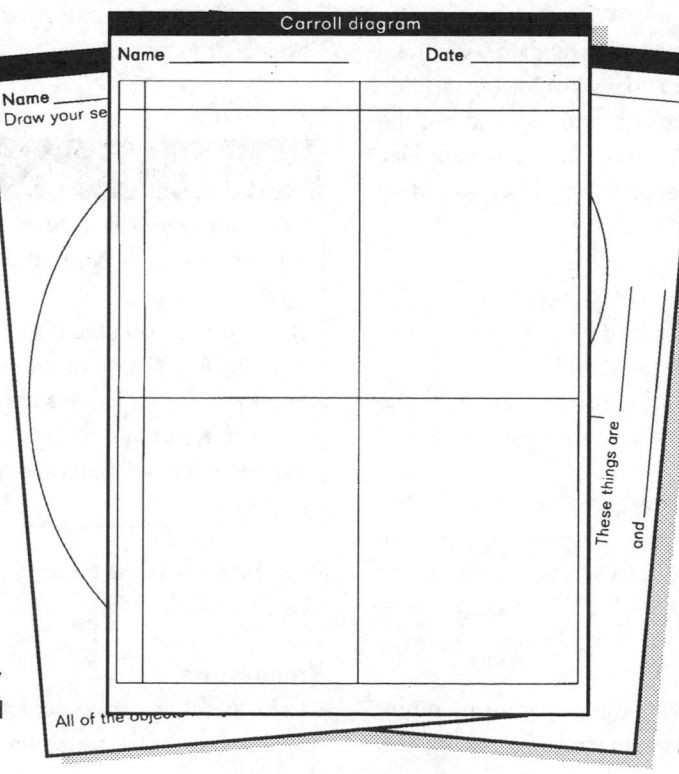

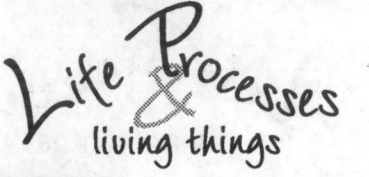

EXPLORING SOUND

We use our sense of hearing to listen to and recognise sounds.

†† Class or group activity, preferably eight to twelve children.

🕐 30 minutes.

Previous skills/knowledge needed
You may find that the children are more receptive to this activity if they have already been out into the local environment to listen to and notice sound.

Preparation
Tape a collection of familiar sounds from a variety of sources, for example sounds of vehicles, a pedestrian crossing beep, a doorbell or a telephone. Do this with the children as a class activity, or use commercial sound tapes. Prepare a set of picture cards to match the sound sources.

Resources needed
A collection of sounds and a set of pictures to match.

Language to be introduced
Sound, noise, hear, listen, volume, loud, louder, loudest, noisy, noisier, noisiest, quiet, quieter, quietest, faint, short, long, high, low, rattle, knocking, tuneful.

What to do
Talk to the children about their sense of hearing. Ask them which part of the body they use to hear with. Tell the children they are going to play a sound game, then spread out the pictures of sound sources in the centre of the group. Play the sounds one at a time and, after each one, ask the children what they can tell you about it:
▲ Does it make a lot of noise?
▲ Is it a high/low/loud/soft/long/short sound?
▲ How do you think the sound is made?
▲ Do you know what is making the sound?

Any child who identifies a source correctly can take the corresponding picture. Whoever has the most pictures at the end wins the game.

Once the children have played the game a number of times it can be set up as a 'listening corner' in the classroom with tapes and matching pictures. Children can then play the game in pairs.

Suggestion(s) for extension
Sort the sounds according to volume, length, pitch, pleasantness, rattles, animal noises, machine noises, sounds which give messages. Can the children identify the loudest, quietest, highest, lowest, shortest, longest sound?

Suggestion(s) for support
If there are children in your class with hearing impairment you may need an extra helper to sit with them to play the game on a one-to-one basis.

Assessment opportunities
Make a note of the children who are able to distinguish between loud/soft/gradation of sound. This activity can indicate children who have not previously been identified as having hearing loss or auditory discrimination difficulties.

Opportunities for IT
The tape recorder should be seen as an item of IT equipment. It allows children to save and retrieve sounds, play them back, and even undertake some simple forms of editing. Children should be taught how to use the various controls of the tape recorder and could then make their own sound game for other children to use.

Display ideas
Children's drawings of the sound sources can be displayed. An interactive display for the children to repeat this activity can be made in a quiet corner of the classroom.

Other aspects of the Science PoS covered
Experimental and Investigative Science – 2a.
Physical Processes – 3c.

TASTE

We use our sense of taste to recognise flavours.

†† Individuals within groups of four to eight.

🕐 15 minutes.

*⚠ Impress upon the children that they **must not** put anything into their mouths to taste unless an adult they know has said it is safe to do so. Nuts should **not** be used. It is also a good idea to check with parents that diabetics and children with allergies can take part in this activity.*

Previous skills/knowledge needed
None required.

Preparation
Check that there are no children in your class who react to certain foods. It is not uncommon for children to have allergies

and reactions to dairy products, oranges, chocolate and food colourings. Avoiding any problem items that have been identified, select four food samples for the activity. Ask the children to wash their hands before taking part in this activity.

Resources needed
Small pieces of food in sealed containers so that the children cannot see or smell the contents (suitable foods include cheese, carrot, salt, apple, chocolate, oranges and sugar-free mints), blindfolds, sheets of paper for the children to record the smells.

Language to be introduced
Sweet, sour, salty, sugary, bitter, soft, crunchy, fruity, minty, smooth, juicy, tasty, chewy.

What to do
Gather a group of children together and explain that they are going to use their sense of taste to identify the food in the containers. Ask them if they can tell you which part of their body they use to taste with. Tell them that you have chosen foods which are safe to eat and pleasant to taste.

Explain the rules of the game:
▲ No peeping.
▲ No saying out loud what they think the food is.
▲ They are only allowed to answer 'yes' or 'no'.

Blindfold or ask one child to close his eyes. If blindfolds are not available the other children in the group should turn around so they can't see. Ask the blindfolded child to open his mouth and put his tongue out. Place a small piece of a food, such as cheese, on the tongue and allow him to eat it. Remind him only to answer yes or no, then ask him if he thinks he is able to identify the flavour. Repeat the process with another child. Continue until every child in the group has had the chance to taste all of the food items.

Ask the children to think of words to describe the flavours they have tasted.
▲ Which was your favourite/least favourite flavour? Why?
▲ Were any of the flavours sour, sweet, bitter or salty?
▲ Were some flavours easier to identify than others?
▲ Did your other senses help you to identify some of the flavours (the crunching sound of the carrot, the smell of the orange or the texture of the cheese)?
▲ Can you think of a food which is not safe to eat and give reasons why?

Children could record the tastes by drawing a picture of each food in order on a sheet of paper.

Suggestion(s) for extension
Explore how different flavours affect our sense of taste. Give the children a drink of orange squash (sugar- and additive-free) or fruit juice. Next, give them a mint sweet to chew or suck, then ask them to have another taste of the fruit drink. Ask them:

▲ What do you notice about the taste of the orange?
▲ Why do you think the taste has changed?

Suggestion(s) for support
Some children will not have the language skills necessary to describe the tastes and may need to be told that oranges can be sour, sugar is sweet and so on. An adult helper could talk to the children individually after they have identified what the tastes are and help them to add descriptive words to their recording sheets.

Assessment opportunities
Make a note of the children who were able or unable to identify the foods, and who were able to use appropriate language to describe the flavours and give reasons how they made the identification.

Opportunities for IT
Young children could use a simple word processor linked to a concept keyboard to record their work. The concept keyboard could show pictures of the various foods tasted, with another section providing simple sentences for children to match with the food picture. Older or more able children could write the sentences themselves using the computer keyboard.

Display ideas
Food should not be kept on display but pictures of the food can be displayed with appropriate language.

Other aspects of the Science PoS covered
Experimental and Investigative Science – 2a.

SMELLING POTS

We use our sense of smell to be aware of our world.

†† *Individuals within groups of about ten children.*

🕐 *20 minutes.*

⚠ *The children should be told that it can be dangerous to smell some substances. Reassure them that the items chosen are known to be safe.*

Previous skills/knowledge needed
None required.

Preparation
Prepare a set of 'smelling' pots – cover some yoghurt pots with foil and punch a number of small perforations (suitable smells to use are flower petals, orange segments, coffee, vinegar and mint essence).

Number the pots 1 to 5. Prepare a pot with chocolate for introducing the activity.

Resources needed
Smelling pots (as described above), copies of the photocopiable sheet on page 117.

Language to be introduced
Strong, sweet, fruity, pleasant, unpleasant.

What to do
Pass the pot containing chocolate around and ask the children if they can think of a word to describe the smell. Ask them if they like the smell and why. Spend a few minutes talking to the children about when they use their sense of smell and how their bodies react to it, for example:

▲ When they smell food they like to eat, it makes them feel hungry and makes their mouths water.

▲ When they smell smoke or gas it makes them realise there is danger.

▲ Pepper makes them sneeze, onion makes their eyes water.

(At this point, it may be appropriate to explain the dangers of smelling unknown substances.)

Ask the children which part of the body they smell with. Encourage them to suggest smells they like and dislike, explaining why.

Introduce the pots to the activity at this point, explaining that each pot contains something which has a pleasant smell, and that you want them to identify these smells.

Show them the photocopiable sheet and point out that the pictures of the pots are numbered, matching the numbers on the actual pots. Demonstrate by holding each pot in turn next to its picture so that the children can see the numbers. Explain that you want them to smell the contents of each pot in turn and, when they think they know what is making the smell, to draw or write it in its matching pot on the worksheet.

Suggestion(s) for extension
Make some pots with more unusual smells such as ginger, coriander, cloves, cola, fish or yeast. Allow the children to think of words to describe what they *think* of the smells, rather than trying to identify them.

Suggestion(s) for support
Some children may need additional help to describe the smells. You may also find it appropriate to adapt the photocopiable sheet, giving the children freedom to draw the item they can smell in the pot, then label them with your help.

Assessment opportunities
To help assess whether the children can use their sense of smell, ask them questions such as:

▲ What do you think smell number 1 is?

▲ Why do you think that?

▲ Do you like the smell?

▲ Can you describe the smell?

Opportunities for IT
Pupils could collect data from the class about favourite smells. These could be recorded using a simple graphing package and the results printed out for display purposes. This could lead to further discussion about why children like certain smells and not others.

Display ideas
Display 'smelly' words around pictures representing smells the children like and dislike.

Other aspects of the Science PoS covered
Experimental and Investigative Science – 2a.

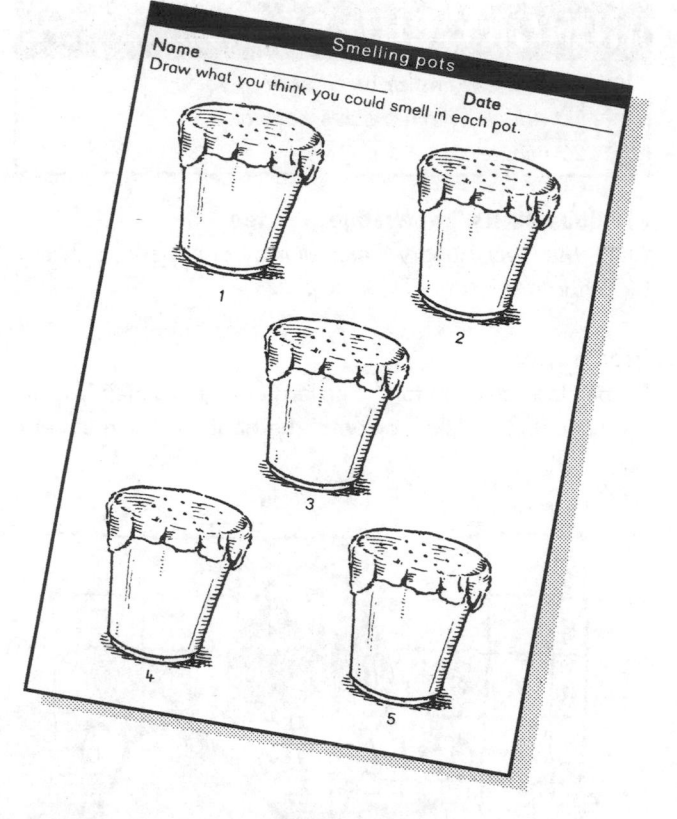

Name _____
Smelling pots
Draw what you think you could smell in each pot.   Date _____

1

2

3

4

5

Reference to photocopiable sheet
The photocopiable sheet on page 117 is a simple recording sheet on which pupils can record the items they think they can smell in the numbered pots.

OUR BITS AND PIECES

To recognise and name the parts of the body.
†† *Class or group activity.*
🕑 *30 minutes.*

Previous skills/knowledge needed
Practical activities about the parts of the body including the game 'Simon says' and the song 'Heads and shoulders, knees and toes' to which words for other parts of the body can be substituted.

Preparation
Try to acquire a shop dummy or make a large cut-out model of a person. Alternatively you may wish to use a pupil as a real-life model.

Make tie-on labels, writing in the parts of the body you wish to teach, and preparing some blank labels for the children's suggestions.

Resources needed
A model of a person, labels (some completed, some blank), sufficient copies of the photocopiable sheets on pages 118 and 119 for your class.

Language to be introduced
Ankle, arm, body, elbow, fingers, foot, feet, hand, head, knee, leg, toes, heel, knuckles, neck, shoulder, waist, wrist, cheek, chin, ear, eye, forehead, hair, mouth, nose.

What to do
Gather the children around your model and play 'Matching the body part'. Point to a part of the model's body and ask the children to point to the same part on their own bodies. Invite them to name that part and, if successful, label that part on the model. Ask the children if they know the name of another part of the body and if they can show you where it is. Continue until you are satisfied the children have learned those parts you want them to, or have shown you the parts they can identify.

When the game is over the children can use a copy of the photocopiable sheet on page 118 to record their knowledge.

Suggestion(s) for extension
More able pupils will probably already know some of the body parts so you will need to proceed at a faster rate or merely give them the resources and ask them to label those parts they know. The parts they fail to name can then be introduced and taught. The photocopiable sheets on pages 118 and 119 will provide evidence of more detailed knowledge and understanding of body parts, including facial features.

Suggestion(s) for support
Any children who have not made a start with reading may need to be paired with a more able reader for the recording part of this activity.

Assessment opportunities
The photocopiable sheets on pages 118 and 119 will provide evidence of which body parts individual children can identify and name.

Opportunities for IT
Children could use framework software like *My World*. This enables the teacher to prepare a picture of the human body

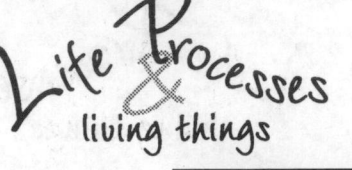
and the appropriate labels so that children can then position the labels against the appropriate parts of the body and print out their labelled picture. A similar activity could be done with a word processor which can handle pictures. The teacher could set up a page with a picture of a child on it and pupils could then label the various parts.

Display ideas
Display the model with the labels attached, or ask the children to draw round one of their group and label the parts of the body.

Draw and label the features on a large picture of a head.

Other aspects of the Science PoS covered
None.

Reference to photocopiable sheets
The photocopiable sheets on pages 118 and 119 can be used as progressive assessment sheets to provide evidence of the children's knowledge of body parts. Pupils are asked to match the words to the correct body part, so it may be necessary to read the words to less able readers.

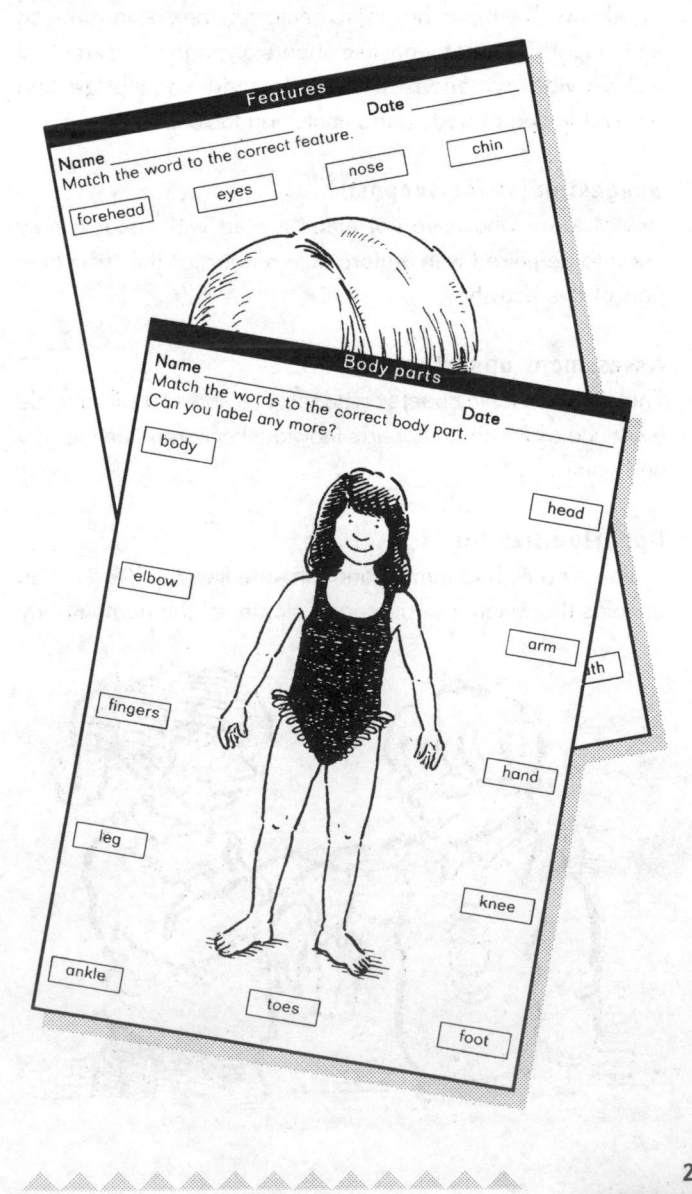

HUNGRY CHILDREN

We need to eat and drink to stay alive.
†† *Individuals within a class activity.*
⏰ *20 minutes.*

Previous skills/knowledge needed
Read *The Very Hungry Caterpillar* by Eric Carle, published by Picture Puffin.

Preparation
Prepare a large chart for the children to record their favourite food and drink. Make copies of the photocopiable sheet on page 120.

Resources needed
The Very Hungry Caterpillar by Eric Carle (Picture Puffin), the prepared chart, copies of the photocopiable sheet on page 120, crayons, adhesive, 10cm × 10cm squares of white paper.

Language to be introduced
Favourite, food, drink, hungry, thirsty, eat.

What to do
Read the story of *The Very Hungry Caterpillar* if you haven't already done so. Ask the children what they would have chosen to eat and drink if *they* were the hungry caterpillar. After their suggestions ask them *why* they would choose these things.

Discuss with the children what they eat and drink, then make a list of all the items the children have eaten and drunk recently.

Ask the children why they think they eat and drink. Some will tell you that they will die if they don't. Others may say that they need food to stay healthy and to give them energy. Hand out the paper squares and crayons and ask the children to draw a picture of their favourite food and a picture of their favourite drink. These can then be transferred to the chart to form a pictogram.

Suggestion(s) for extension

Some pupils could represent the information in a block graph and, after discussion, write a simple interpretation of the information displayed.

Suggestion(s) for support

The younger or less able children will need direction on where to stick their pictures on the chart. It may be necessary to discuss what they are doing individually or in pairs to check that they understand why they are recording the information.

Assessment opportunities

Make a note of the children who do/do not know that we need to eat and drink to stay alive.

Opportunities for IT

Children could collect information about the favourite food and drinks of pupils in their class. This could be done by the whole class, by individuals or groups of children. Older or more able children could collect information from different classes. The data collected could be presented using a simple graphing package – some packages enable children to use pictures and thus produce a pictogram, others provide the facility to draw block graphs or pie charts. In most cases the number of categories, or blocks, is limited, so some preparatory work needs to be done to decide the range of favourite foods which should be included.

Alternatively children could use a simple data base and enter favourite and least favourite foods against the name of the child. The field names might be:

name	*Kuldip*
sex	*boy*
like	*rice*
dislike	*carrots*

Children could use the data entered to draw graphs of liked or disliked foods or to answer questions such as:

▲ How many children don't like carrots?

▲ How many boys like carrots?

Display ideas

The pictogram and individual block graphs can be mounted and displayed with the children's writing and paintings of food and drink, or pictures cut from magazines.

Other aspects of the Science PoS covered

Experimental and Investigative Science – 2b, 2c, 3a, 3b.

Reference to photocopiable sheet

The photocopiable sheet on page 120 is a block graph on to which the children can individually transfer the information collected during the group activity. You may wish to retain this as evidence to support a number of assessment activities, including the ability to use block graphs to represent results. Enter the information on the horizontal axis before photocopying or ask the children to do this themselves. Pupils may then write a few sentences on the back of the sheet, if they are able to interpret the information.

HEALTH AND HAPPINESS

Eating the right food is important to our health.

†† *Whole class working in groups of six to eight children.*

⏰ *30 minutes.*

Previous skills/knowledge needed
The children should know that they need to eat and drink to stay alive.

Preparation
Make a collection of labels, packaging and pictures based on the children's favourite foods and healthy foods.

Resources needed
A collection of food pictures, labels and packaging, copies of the photocopiable sheet on page 121, *The Very Hungry Caterpillar* by Eric Carle (Picture Puffin), set rings.

Language to be introduced
Healthy, overweight, sugar, protein, vitamins, fat.

What to do
Either start with the story *The Very Hungry Caterpillar* or a graph of the children's favourite foods. Ask them why they like the foods they have chosen. You will get a variety of responses and may even be lucky enough to have some children responding that it is because it helps to keep them

healthy. If not, you should introduce this idea yourself. With very young children you may have to establish what is meant by 'keep them healthy'.

Develop discussion about whether their favourite foods alone will keep them healthy, why we need to eat other types of foods and what happens to us if we eat too much food. Ask them what happened to the very hungry caterpillar when he ate too much of the wrong kind of food on Saturday. How did he make himself feel better? Show the children the pictures, labels and packaging you have collected. Sort the items, asking the children if they think the foods and drinks are good for them. Alternatively let pupils choose their own criteria for sorting.

When each group of children in the class has completed this activity (working simultaneously, or taking it in turns, depending on the number of resources available), they can report their opinions to each other, comparing the sets they have made.

The groups can record their findings on group recording sheets which can then be used as a class display. The children could also make 'Healthy eating' posters to display around the school.

Suggestion(s) for extension
Ask the children to sort the pictures, labels and/or packaging according to the ingredients and additives.

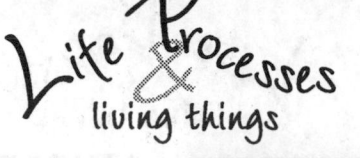
▲ Are they able to conclude which additives are the most/ least used?

▲ What do they notice about the foods which contain the most fat/protein/vitamins?

Suggestion(s) for support

Check if any pupils are vegetarian and be sensitive to overweight children, or those with relatives who are overweight.

Assessment opportunities

The photocopiable sheet on page 121 will enable you to collect evidence of the children who know which foods are good for them.

Display ideas

Pictures of food and drink can be attached with Blu-Tack to an interactive display of food and drink which are good for us/not good for us. Children should be encouraged to bring examples of their own, giving reasons for their choices.

Other aspects of the Science PoS covered

Experimental and Investigative Science – 3b.

Reference to photocopiable sheets

The photocopiable sheet on page 121 is an open-ended sheet on which children can record their own ideas on which foods are healthy and which foods are not. This could be used immediately after the activity or at a later date to assess retained knowledge and understanding.

EXERCISE IS HEALTHY

We need to exercise to keep healthy.

†† *Class activity.*

🕐 *20 minutes.*

⚠ *The children should be allowed to decide when to withdraw from vigorous exercise. **Never** insist on children continuing to exercise beyond their limits.*

Previous skills/knowledge needed

None required.

Preparation

Make sure that the hall or playground is available for your use.

Resources needed

None.

Language to be introduced

Heat, sweating, panting, exercise, pulse, beating, faster, heart, out of breath, breathing.

What to do

Tell the children that you are going to play a game of tag so that you can find out if exercise makes anything happen to their bodies. At this point you can ask the children to predict what they think might happen.

Take the children into the hall or outside for a game of tag. Initially the child who is caught should then become the child who is 'on'. Once you have assessed which children are fit and able to keep going without being put under stress, you can develop the game by selecting the fittest as a group of catchers. When the other children are 'tagged', or caught, they are out of the game and should return to where you are standing.

Keeping an eye on the game, as the children return, ask them about any changes in their bodies that they are aware of. If they have been running for a while, they may notice that they are warmer, sweating and that their hearts are beating faster.

You may wish to play the game several times before you are satisfied all the children have a fair idea of what happens to their bodies after exercise.

On returning to the classroom, spend five minutes discussing why it is important to take exercise, even though it makes us out of breath.

Ask the children how much time in the day they spend sitting down, running around or sleeping?

The children can record individually the changes that happened either in writing or pictures.

Suggestion(s) for extension

Older or more able children can be encouraged to feel for

their pulse. Explain that it is their heart beating that they are feeling. Play the game again and this time at the end ask the children to feel their pulse again.

▲ What do you notice?

▲ Can you count the number of beats?

▲ How much faster is your heart beating?

▲ How do you know?

Suggestion(s) for support
Be sensitive to children who are overweight or unfit for any reason. Only allow them to do what they can manage.

Assessment opportunities
Most children will be able to describe some of the changes to their bodies. The more able will identify that their hearts are beating faster. Some may know that the heart is a muscle or a pump and needs exercise to stay healthy.

Display ideas
Display the children's pictures of themselves before, during and after exercise!

Other aspects of the Science PoS covered
Experimental and Investigative Science – 1b, 2b, 2c, 3a, 3c, 3e.
Life Processes and Living Things – 1b.

MEDICINE AND DRUGS

We sometimes need medicines or pills to make us well.

†† *Class activity.*

🕐 *30 minutes.*

Preparation
Check that no one in the class has recently had a death in the family.

Resources needed
Empty bottles which contained medicine and pills, a suitable story as a starting point, such as *Going to the Doctor* by Anne Civardi (Usborne First Experiences) or 'Miss Polly had a dolly' from *This Little Puffin* compiled by Elizabeth Matterson.

Language to be introduced
Pills, tablets, medicine, ill, symptoms, drugs, doctor, stethoscope, temperature, thermometer.

What to do
Read 'Miss Polly had a dolly', *Going to the Doctor* or a similar story. If any pupils in the class have recently been ill, you could ask them to relate what happened to them and what made them better.

Talk about some of the symptoms that you may have if you are ill such as a headache, rash or a sore throat.

▲ What does a doctor do to find out what is wrong?

▲ What does he/she do to make people better?

▲ From which shop do you buy medicines?

Talk about medicines:

▲ What colour are they?

▲ What are pills like?

▲ What do they taste like?

Discuss what happens if you take too much medicine or too many pills, and the dangers of drugs.

Ask the children why they think the bottles say 'Keep out of reach of children'. What should they do if they find any medicines or pills? Talk about the adults who are allowed to give them medicines and pills, and what they should do if anyone else offers them to them.

The children can make posters and write slogans about not touching medicines and pills. These can be displayed around the school.

Suggestion(s) for extension

Talk to the children about other harmful substances which should not be eaten or drunk. Look at the various 'Not to be swallowed' labels found on household cleaners and ask the children why they are there. Discuss the fact that they can be easily seen and recognised by their shape, logo and colour. Words are not necessary as the picture gives very strict instructions. The photocopiable sheet on page 122 may be useful for this activity.

Suggestion(s) for support

There may be children in the class who have to take long-term medication for a medical condition. Invite the children concerned to talk to the rest of the class about how and why they take their medication.

Assessment opportunities

Allow the children to talk freely about their own experiences of feeling ill, visiting the doctor and how they were cured. In a discussion like this teachers may discover the presence of drugs in a child's home. Note which children understand the dangers of pills and medicines and know not to touch them.

Opportunities for IT

Children could use a word processor to write simple slogans about the use of drugs. They could experiment with letter sizes, fonts and even colours to make their message stand out more clearly.

Older or more able children might look at the kind of information found on medicine bottles and produce their own

label. They could extend this type of writing by producing a label for a packet of their favourite sweets – one to be taken after meals three times a day!

Display ideas

Display items the doctor may use to diagnose illness, such as a stethoscope or a thermometer. Turn the home corner into a doctor's surgery for the children to participate in role play.

Other aspects of the Science PoS covered

None.

Reference to photocopiable sheet

Photocopiable sheet 122 will provide reinforcement about the dangers of medicines, pills, drugs, poisons and other harmful substances. You should discuss this sheet with the children before they complete it in order to re-emphasise the very real dangers of the products displaying the labels. Can the children think of any more?

BABIES

Humans have babies which grow into children and then adults.

†† *Class activity.*

🕐 *40 minutes.*

Previous skills/knowledge needed

None required.

Preparation

Ask a mum (or dad) with a new baby (three to six months old) to bring him or her in to visit the class. Discuss with the mum the resources she will need, and the areas of the baby's care she would like to talk about. She may even be willing to give the baby a bath! Make sure that the room is warm with no draughts and check that nobody in the class has had an infectious illness recently.

Resources needed

You will need to be guided by mum on the resources she will need: she may well bring her own. A photograph of yourself as a baby, copies of the photocopiable sheet on page 123.

Language to be introduced

Care, older, younger.

What to do

Sit the children in a circle so that they can see both mum and baby clearly.

Introduce mum and baby to the children, then talk about how old the baby is, how much time he sleeps, how much

Suggestion(s) for support

For a number of reasons, there may be children in the class who do not possess baby photographs. Be aware that not all children belong to the traditional family group of father, mother, brothers and sisters.

Assessment opportunities

Assess which children know they grew from babies and will eventually become adults.

Opportunities for IT

If children bring in photographs of themselves as babies they could word process their own labels for a display. More able pupils could extend the writing by adding extra comments about the picture.

Display ideas

Make a large display of a life development picture of human beings.

Display recent photographs of the children in a sequence with their own baby and toddler photos.

Other aspects of the Science PoS covered

Life Processes and Living Things – 1b.

Reference to photocopiable sheet

The photocopiable sheet on page 123 offers a number of pictures of human beings at different stages in human life. Children can cut out and arrange the pictures in order.

and what he eats, the care that he needs. Discuss with the children what the baby can do for himself now and ask them to suggest what he will be able to do as he gets older. Ask the children if they have any questions they want to ask before they watch mum bath, dry and dress the baby.

The baby will then need to be fed, either with the children present or in a separate quiet room set aside for the purpose.

Talk to the children about how much care the baby needs now and how much in the future. Show them a photograph of yourself as a baby and ask them how you have changed. Talk to them about how you learned to do certain things and how one day *they* will be grown-ups and able to look after themselves. Let the children sort the pictures on the photocopiable sheet on page 123.

Suggestion(s) for extension

Set up a display of recent photographs of the children and when they were babies. Are they able to match recent photographs of themselves to the correct baby? Include photographs of staff if they will allow their baby photographs to be used.

SCIENCE

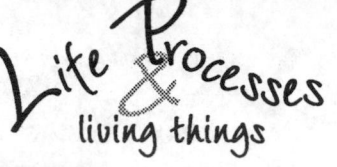
GROWING CHILDREN

We all grow.

†† *Paired activity in ability groups of six to eight children.*

🕐 *45 minutes.*

Previous skills/knowledge needed

The children should have some experience of collecting and representing information.

Preparation

Gather the measuring resources the children will need to use. Photocopy enough worksheets (page 120) for children to have one between two.

Resources needed

Cubes, straws, string, metre- and centimetre-rulers, tape-measures, weighing scales.

Language to be introduced

Tall, taller, tallest, short, shorter, shortest, long, longer, longest, metre, centimetre, standard measures, span.

What to do

Put your children into ability groups according to their measuring experience. Working with one group at a time, explain that you want them to find out who is the tallest child in their group. This information can be found out in a number of ways. Ask younger or less able children to draw round and cut out the outline of each other. When they have finished, gather the group together and ask them to put the outlines in order of height starting with the shortest or the tallest,

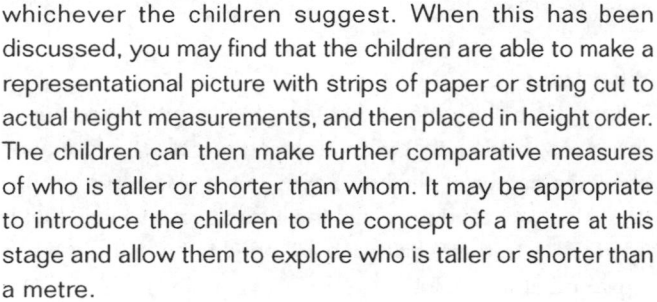

whichever the children suggest. When this has been discussed, you may find that the children are able to make a representational picture with strips of paper or string cut to actual height measurements, and then placed in height order. The children can then make further comparative measures of who is taller or shorter than whom. It may be appropriate to introduce the children to the concept of a metre at this stage and allow them to explore who is taller or shorter than a metre.

Some children will be able to take measurements using straws, cubes, spans and other non-standard measures. Working in pairs, pupils can measure each other's heights in straws, spans or pencils. They can combine their information with the other members of their group and transfer it on to block graphs. The photocopiable sheet on page 120 may be useful for this.

The more able can measure with metres and centimetres and display the information in bar charts.

At the end of the activity, the children can analyse the information:

▲ Who is the tallest or shortest in your group?

▲ Why do you think some children are taller or shorter than others?

▲ Are there other measurements you can make?

Suggestion(s) for extension

All groups can collect measurements to answer questions like:

▲ Who is the heaviest or lightest in the class?

▲ Who has the longest reach, the longest hand, the widest reach?

▲ Who can hold the most cubes in their hand?

▲ What does this tell us about the size of their hands?

The children should use the measurements appropriate to their level of ability. The more able will be able to collect information on the children in the class and not just their group.

Suggestion(s) for support

Be sensitive to children who are particularly short or tall, so they do not become uncomfortable about their size. Choose a different measurement for collection if you wish – the learning objective does not rely on height measurement, but simply on the fact that there will be differences in the measurements and that we all grow.

Assessment opportunities

Most children will be able to tell you that they grow. This activity will give them the evidence to support that theory. The more able may see a simple relationship between some of the measurements, for example, the tallest child has the

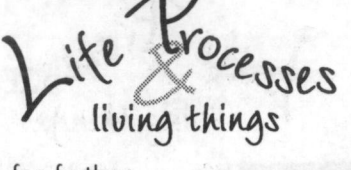
longest reach. This can form the hypothesis for further investigation if you wish.

Opportunities for IT

Children could collect their own measurements and enter them into a database which has already been prepared by the teacher in advance. There could be a record for each child in which they enter such things as:

name	*Joanne*
boy/girl	*girl*
arm reach	*40cm*
hand span	*12cm*
height	*110cm*
weight	*20kg*
cubes held	*16*

Children could then sort the information to see who had the longest reach, who was the tallest, the shortest, and so on. The information could be printed out as a simple block graph.

Children will need support to enter their data. This can often be provided by parents or other adult helpers. This offers an opportunity to teach children some of the basic

editing aspects and to discuss their understanding of the measurements they are entering.

Alternatively, children could add one measurement into a tally chart for the group or class and then use a graphing program to produce simple block graphs showing the relative heights of the children in their group.

Display ideas

Display cut-out models of the children labelled with a number of measurements alongside the children's charts and graphs.

Block graph   Date ____

Name			
10			
9			
8			
7			
6			
5			
4			
3			
2			
1			
0			

Other aspects of the Science PoS covered

Experimental and Investigative Science – 2b, 2c, 3b, 3c, 3d.

Reference to photocopiable sheet

The photocopiable sheet on page 120 is a block graph on to which the children can transfer the information they collect during the group activity. Enter the information on the horizontal (number of straws) and vertical (number of children) axes before photocopying the sheet, or ask the children to fill this in themselves.

WHAT COLOUR EYES?

Some things about us are different. Some things about us are the same.

†† *Paired activity within ability groups of six to eight children.*

⏰ *30 minutes.*

Previous skills/knowledge needed

The children should have had some experience of collecting information.

Resources needed

Tubs and coloured cubes to match the number of eye colours of children in the class, copies of the tick or tally chart on page 124.

Language to be introduced

Same, different, graph, chart, tally, pictogram, taller, longer, most, least.

What to do

Talk to the children for a few minutes about the colour of their eyes. Explain that you are going to collect information about the colour of children's eyes in the class. The groups of children will need to collect the information in a way that is appropriate to their ability and will need to have the method explained at this point.

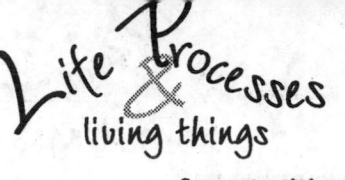
Suggestion(s) for extension

More able children may collect information using a tick or tally chart (p124). The collected information can then be transferred to block graphs and bar charts respectively.

The information can be compared at the end of the activity and a note made of how many children have each eye colour. Do the graphs match? To help the children assess their results ask questions like:

▲ What colour eyes do you have?

▲ What colour eyes does your friend have?

▲ Do we all have the same colour eyes?

▲ How many different eye colours are there?

▲ How can we find out how many children have blue/green/brown eyes?

▲ How many children had blue/green/brown eyes?

▲ How do we know?

▲ Which eye colour did most/least children have?

▲ Did we all have the same/different eye colour?

Suggestion(s) for support

Younger and less able children should be able to draw a picture of their own eyes which can then be displayed in the correct column of a pictogram. Alternatively the children can collect a matching coloured cube for each child's eye colour, using one-to-one correspondence. These cubes can be built into towers of one colour and possibly transferred to coloured squares to form a block graph (page 120).

Assessment opportunities

The children will probably tell you that some eyes were the same colour and some were different.

The more able may suggest other features people have which can be the same or different, such as hair colour. These can then be investigated further if you wish.

Opportunities for IT

The information collected can be entered into a graphing package so that children can produce block graphs, pictograms or pie charts showing the colour of eyes of pupils in the class. It is important that the class agree on the range of colours to be used. Will there be a category for hazel eyes, or are they included under brown?

Display ideas

Display the children's graphs alongside pictures of people's faces which show a variety of eye colour.

Other aspects of the Science PoS covered

Experimental and Investigative Science – 2c, 3b.

Reference to photocopiable sheets

The photocopiable sheet on page 120 is a simple block graph on which the children can record frequency of eye colour in the class. They should colour one square for each cube collected or for each tick on their collection sheet, according to the method they use. Page 124 provides a basic tick or tally chart for children to use, according to their ability.

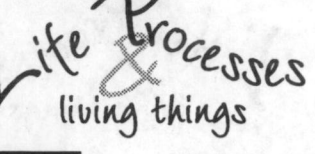

SORTING SEEDS

Seeds have observable similarities and differences.

†† *Children in groups. This lesson could be taught to the whole class split into groups or to groups in turn.*

🕐 *40 minutes.*

⚠ *Be careful to choose non-poisonous seeds which have not been dressed with insecticide. Young children should be warned **not** to put the seeds into their ears and noses.*

Previous skills/knowledge needed

The learning opportunities in this lesson will be enhanced if the children have been given previous experience of sorting.

Preparation

Collect a number of seeds, trying to include variations in size, shape and colour. Consider seeds from a range of plant types such as trees, vegetables, fruit (including pips and stones) and flowers. These could be collected in a previous teaching activity, or by the children themselves from sunflower heads, melons, pumpkins, pomegranates and so on.

Resources needed

A variety of seeds, hand magnifiers, microscope, set rings, large sheets of paper, PVA adhesive, copies of recording sheets, as appropriate (pages 114–116).

Language to be introduced

White, thin, small, striped, bumpy, smooth, dry, shiny, round, larger, smaller, centimetre.

What to do

Talk to the children as a class or group about the seeds. Invite them to express their ideas about seeds, where they come from and their function. Ask the children to look closely at the seeds and say what they notice:

▲ How are the seeds different?

▲ Is there anything which is the same about them?

Help the children identify similarities and differences and sort the collection according to their own criteria. The criteria should include size, shape and colour. Demonstrate the use of sorting rings to create sets. Can any of the children think of a way to measure the seeds? Some may be able to lay them out in order of size, others may suggest sorting by whether the seeds are larger or smaller than a centimetre.

When the children have finished their sorting ask them to glue the seeds onto large sheets of paper, or to draw the seeds in their groups.

Some may be able to draw and label two seeds to show their differences.

Suggestion(s) for extension

Those children who readily suggest sorting by size, shape and colour can be encouraged to develop their thinking by sorting according to unobserved criteria such as the type of plant a seed comes from or the method by which the seeds are dispersed.

Suggestion(s) for support

The lesson could be repeated with pupils who are unable to sort the seeds without help. Encourage them to find more seeds to add to the sets which have already been created.

Assessment opportunities

Watch the children as they carry out the sorting activities and listen to their conversations. Most Key Stage 1 children will be able to sort according to colour, size and shape. You may like to make a note of those who find this basic activity difficult so that they can be given more practice. Children functioning at a higher level may be able to:

▲ use the magnifiers effectively;

▲ create overlapping sets and subsets;

▲ make plausible suggestions as to which plants the seeds may grow into;

▲ suggest more advanced headings for sorting such as weight, texture, smell and so on;

▲ suggest ideas for recording and further investigation.

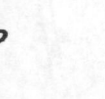

Opportunities for IT

More able children could use a prepared branching database to identify their seeds. The database could be set up in advance by the teacher, or even older pupils in the school. This type of software works like a key, asking questions which require a yes/no answer until it arrives at the name of the seed the child has selected. Children could add seeds of their own after they have got used to the way of phrasing questions, but they may need initial support for this activity.

Display ideas

Photograph the sorted seeds.
Create an interactive seeds display.
Display the seeds next to pictures of their parent plant.

Other aspects of the Science PoS covered

Experimental and Investigative Science – 2a, 2b, 2c, 3a, 3c.

Reference to photocopiable sheets

The photocopiable sheets on pages 114, 115 and 116 are blank Venn and Carroll diagram sheets which can be used for any further sorting activities. Photocopy one sheet and enter the sorting label before making the number of copies you need.

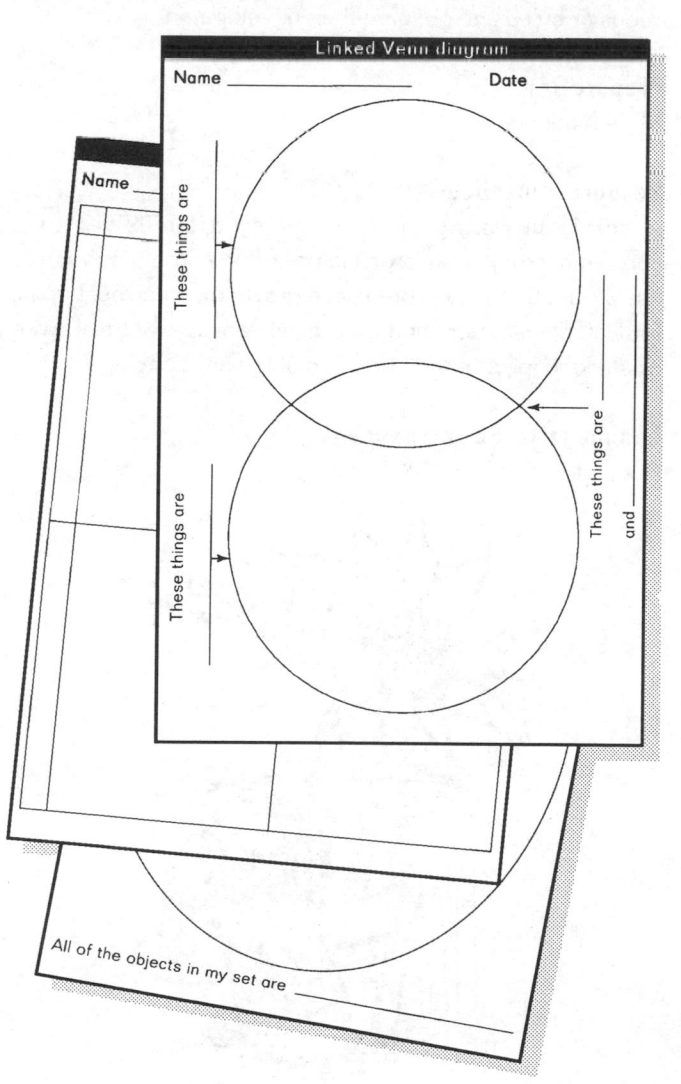

PLANTING SEEDS

Seeds grow into plants.

✝✝ *Whole class in groups of six children.*

🕐 *30 minutes.*

⚠ *Warn the children **not** to put the seeds into ears, noses or mouths. Use seeds which have not been dressed with insecticide.*

Previous skills/knowledge needed

None required.

Preparation

Check the seed packet to find out the conditions necessary for growth. Some seeds need light for germination to take place, others must be in the dark. Some seeds need to be watered from the bottom, others from the top. As a general rule, seeds should be sown at a depth equivalent to their diameter. Make sure that the seed compost is damp.

Resources needed

Seed compost, seed trays or suitable containers, labels, trowels and a variety of seeds such as mustard, cress, courgettes, beans and potatoes. These seeds are particularly suitable as they are easy to grow, grow quickly and the root growth is visible if grown in glass or clear plastic containers. The bottom half of a plastic drinks bottle makes a good pot, and you can use the tops of the bottles as mini-cloches.

Language to be introduced

Germination, compost, trowel, seed trays, growth.

What to do

Gather the class around a table and give each child some seeds to handle. Spend a short time discussing their texture, size, colour and which plant they came from. Allow the children to feel the compost and express their opinions on the texture.

Give each small group of children a container, trowel, seed compost and seeds. Demonstrate in stages how to plant the seeds, giving the children time to copy each stage as you do it.

Talk to the children about the conditions the seeds need for growth. They should be encouraged to suggest suitable places for the seeds to be kept until germination takes place. Follow the instructions on the seed packets to tend the young plants correctly.

Records of any significant changes can be made with pictures and diaries either as a class activity or individually. Significant growth could be measured comparatively using Multilink cube towers, lengths of string, or the standard units of centimetres.

Suggestion(s) for extension

Some children will be able to record new growth individually, recording dates of germination, leaf growth, and flower development. They could measure plant growth in centimetres and record the information in graphical form.

Suggestion(s) for support

Younger children may need additional help to use the equipment and to sow the seeds evenly. It may be advisable to reduce the size of the teaching group or to use an adult helper.

Assessment opportunities

Most of the children will know that seeds grow into plants. Questioning will enable you to note those children who realise that seeds grow into the plants they come from.

Opportunities for IT

Older pupils could use a word processor to keep a simple diary of their seeds either as a class or group activity. They need to be introduced to the way in which their work can be saved and retrieved at a later time.

A graphing package could be used to show the new growth of the plant over a period of several weeks, either as an ongoing project or by using data collected and recorded elsewhere.

Display ideas

Very young or less able children could display new growth in large pictures put together to form a comic strip frieze, with the number of days recorded in a number-line above or below.

Display Multilink towers or lengths of string in height order above a number-of-days number-line.

Display the seeds next to a picture of their parent plant so that the children can compare the plant that they are growing with the end result. Does it look the same?

Other aspects of the Science PoS covered

Experimental and Investigative Science – 2b, 2c, 3a, 3c.
Life Processes and Living Things – 3a, 3c.

LABELLING A PLANT

Recognising and naming the parts of a flowering plant.
†† *Class or group activity.*
🕐 *30 minutes.*

Previous skills/knowledge needed

Children should have had the opportunity to grow plants from seeds or bulbs and observe their development.

Preparation

None required.

Resources needed

A sturdy flowering plant (possibly a sunflower or a chrysanthemum), or a large picture of one. You may wish to use a plant that the children have grown themselves. Labels for leaf, flower, stem and root, blank labels, twist-ties, wire or string, copies of the photocopiable sheet on page 125.

Language to be introduced

Root, stem, leaf, flower, label.

SCIENCE

What to do

Gather the children together in a circle around the plant. Give them time to tell each other what they notice about the plant. Observe the children at this time to check if any of them are already aware of the parts of the plant. If so, they will need to proceed to the extension activity, although you may wish them to complete the photocopiable sheet to support your observations.

Ask the remaining children, individually, to point to and name any part of the plant they know. Carefully attach the appropriate label to the plant or picture. Repeat in this way until the children have recognised and named the leaf, flower, stem and root. Some of the children may offer additional suggestions which can be written on the blank labels. Take the children outside and repeat the activity with a flowering tree if one is available.

Suggestion(s) for support

You may wish to pair poorer readers with partners who are able to read the labels. Some children will not know the names of the parts and may need to repeat the activity in a small group with a different plant.

Suggestion(s) for extension

Give the children a set of blank labels and ask them to label other parts of the plant that they know, such as veins, petals and sepals. They may wish to use hand magnifiers to look more closely at the plant parts and record anything that they notice.

Assessment opportunities

Make a note of those children who can/cannot name the main parts of the plant:
▲ during the introductory discussion;
▲ during the activity;
▲ after the activity.

Use the photocopiable sheet on page 125 to help you assess the children's knowledge.

Opportunities for IT

Children might use teacher-prepared files in framework software like *My World* so that they can 'drag' the relevant labels to the parts of the flower. The final results can be printed out for the child's folder or display in the classroom. Some children might like to draw their own flower using a simple art package and then add the text for the labels.

Labelling a plant

Name _____   Date _____

Write the correct word in each box.

flower   stem   root   leaf

Display ideas

All the children can contribute to an interactive display of a large collage of different kinds of flowering plants. Labels and Blu-Tack will enable them to repeat the naming activity as necessary.

Other aspects of the Science PoS covered

None.

Reference to photocopiable sheet

The photocopiable sheet on page 125 can be used as a recording sheet during the lesson, to reinforce what has been done, or completed some time after the lesson to assess the children's retention of knowledge.

PLANTS NEED LIGHT AND WATER

Plants need sunlight and water to grow.
†† *Class activity.*
🕐 *Several weeks to introduce the activity; 30 minutes for the activity.*

Previous skills/knowledge needed

The children should have planted seeds and have some understanding of the conditions needed for growth.

Preparation

Several weeks before the lesson, take a variety of plants into the classroom and encourage the children to care for them. If possible, include three spider plants and two busy Lizzies as these will be particularly appropriate.

Put two spider plants in a bright position where they will receive plenty of sunlight. Put the third spider plant in a dark place (possibly a cupboard) where the children won't accidentally find it. When you begin the activity it is fun to make a great pretence that one of the spider plants is lost and you can't remember where you put it.

Resources needed

Several plants, including three spider plants and two busy Lizzies.

Language to be introduced

Spider plants, busy Lizzies, green, yellow, wilt, wither, droopy, healthy, sickly.

What to do

When you are satisfied that the spider plant you have hidden in the dark place has taken on a yellowish hue and is beginning to look sickly, take it into the classroom and pretend you have just found it in the cupboard.

Place it next to the healthy-looking spider plants the children have been looking after and bemoan the fact that it doesn't look the same. Ask why the healthy plant looks like it does. Encourage the children to suggest reasons why the other spider plant looks so sick. You will get several suggestions which may include:

▲ you forgot to water it;
▲ the plant had no air;
▲ it was dark in the cupboard;
▲ it was cold in the cupboard.

You could do further work on all of these hypotheses if you wish, but you should certainly investigate the following two.

1 Plants need sunlight

Ask the children to predict what will happen if you put one of the healthy-looking plants in the dark. How will they know if there has been any effect on the plant when they bring it back into the light? Discuss with them whether (and how) they are going to record what the plant looks like before putting it in the dark, and for how long they are going to leave it before checking it.

Put one of the healthy plants in the dark place and keep one in sunlight. Make regular comparisons and note any differences between them. As soon as it becomes obvious that the plant in the dark will die if deprivation of sunlight continues, reintroduce the plant to light and watch its recovery.

Spider plants are good for this investigation as they react fairly quickly.

2 Plants need water

Explain to the children that you are going to find out what happens to plants if you don't water them. Using two identical plants, water one as normal and do not water the other. Make daily comparisons and note any differences between them.

Once it is clear that the unwatered plant will die without water, resume watering and make observations of its recovery.

Busy Lizzies are excellent plants to use for this investigation because they react very quickly to lack of water and revive swiftly when watering is resumed. At the end of the activity the children should be encouraged to evaluate what happened. Ask them about changes they saw in the plant deprived of water, and invite them to give reasons for their opinions. Encourage them to give more than one reason. Ask them what they think would have happened if the plant had been given water, again giving reasons for their opinions. How can they be sure that the plant reacted as it did because it didn't have water?

Suggestion(s) for extension

Investigate what happens to other plants when deprived of light and water.

Suggestion(s) for support

Some children will need to have the plants' reactions pointed out to them. They should record each step of the investigation under supervision, with emphasis put on the reasons for the changes.

Assessment opportunities

You may wish to organise an assessment activity where the children set up their own investigations into one of the other hypotheses suggested during the course of the activity.

Display ideas

Photograph the plant before and after the investigation, then compare the photographs. Alternatively, ask the children to draw the plant before and after.

Make a display of plants, and the children's drawings and accounts, with the title 'All plants need sunlight and water to grow'.

Other aspects of the Science PoS covered

Experimental and Investigative Science – 1a, 1b, 1c, 2a, 2b, 2c, 3a, 3b, 3c, 3d, 3e, 3f.

SUNFLOWER COMPETITION

Seeds grow into plants which produce seeds for their own kind.

†† *Class activity.*

🕐 *40 minutes.*

Previous skills/knowledge needed
It will be helpful if the children have planted other seeds and have some knowledge of the conditions necessary for growth.

Preparation
Prepare a small area for sowing enough sunflower seeds for one plant per child. The seeds should be sown approximately 50–100cm apart.

If no school garden is available, a small area around the perimeter of the field or playground, or large flower pots, will suffice. The grown sunflowers need a spot which is sheltered and sunny and some method of support. Garden string tied from posts across the front is suitable.

The best time for sowing is towards the end of March or the beginning of April.

Resources needed
Sunflower seeds, dibber, lollipop sticks with names, garden string.

Language to be introduced
Plant, sunflower, sow, sowing area, flower pot, centimetre.

What to do
Explain to the children that you are going to have a sunflower growing competition to see which seed grows into the tallest sunflower. Distribute the seeds and spend a short time discussing the size, colour, shape and texture of the seeds. Invite the children to choose two seeds each, then ask them why they have chosen those particular ones. Explain that you are going to plant two seeds in case one doesn't grow. If they both grow, the child can decide which plant to enter in the competition.

Take the children out to the sowing area and explain why you have chosen that spot. Allocate a place for each child to plant their seeds, explaining why they need to leave so much space between each seed even though they are so small!

Plant the seeds approximately one centimetre below the ground, cover and water. Mark the spots with lollipop sticks labelled with the children's names. Water the seeds daily if there is not sufficient rain.

As the plants grow taller, attach the garden string across the posts to hold the flowers in position (the flower heads get very heavy).

Make regular observations. As the plants grow, make a note of the things that children notice about them. When did the leaves and flowers first appear?

When the flower has opened, ask the children why they think it is called a sunflower.

▲ What colour are the petals?

▲ Why are they so bright?

▲ Why is the stem so thick?

▲ Why is the flower so big?

▲ How many centimetres/cubes/straws across is the flower?

▲ How many weeks was it until the sunflowers were taller than the pupils, taller than the teacher?

The children should notice the seeds appearing in the flower heads. These can be harvested in autumn.

The children can make weekly measurements of the height of their sunflower by cutting lengths of string. The less able can then display the lengths of string in sequence to show how the sunflower is growing.

Alternatively, you can ask the children to measure the length of string in metres and centimetres and record this information graphically (see below).

You may also like to make measurements of the flower head, or leaf length and width.

Drawings can also be made of the leaf shape, the flower head, the petals, even the whole sunflower.

Suggestion(s) for extension
When the sunflower seeds have been harvested, estimate, then count the number of seeds, observe the pattern of the seed distribution, cut through the stem to observe the cross-section and count the number of leaves on the heads.

Suggestion(s) for support
Plant a few extra sunflowers in pots in the classroom. These can be used to replace any plants that do not grow.

Assessment opportunities
Make a note of the children who noticed the seeds growing in the flower head. Which children realised that the growing seeds look the same as the ones they started with?

Opportunities for IT
Pupils could use simple graphing software to produce graphs of their sunflower growth. If they add data to their graph over a period of several weeks, this would require saving and retrieving at each entry. Alternatively they could record their data on a duplicated record sheet and enter the full set of measurements towards the end of the project. Children could then make a display of the different sunflower graphs and suggest reasons why some grew more than others.

If more than just height measurements are made, children could add their measurements to a simple database set up in advance by the teacher. This could include name of child, height, size of flower head, leaf length and width. This would have to be done at the final measurement stage to create a class set of data which could be sorted into size order, or children could use the software to create graphs of height, flower head width and so on. More able pupils might be introduced to simple questions like:

▲ 'Does the tallest sunflower have the largest head?'

Sunflowers could only be identified by the name of the grower, unless you give the plants names of their own!

Display ideas
Make a life cycle display like the one shown below.

Other aspects of the Science PoS covered
Experimental and Investigative Science – 2a, 2b. 2c, 3b, 3c.

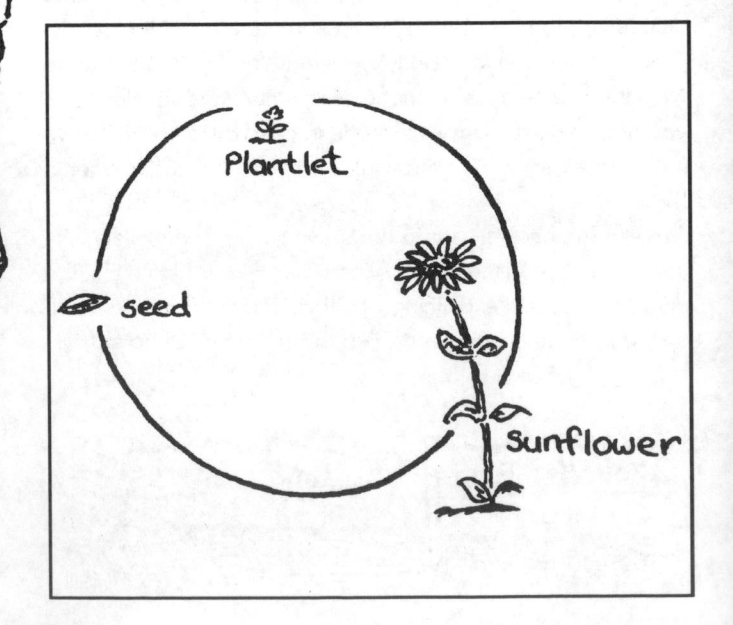

SCIENCE

PLANTS AT SCHOOL

Different plants are found in the school environment.

†† *Class activity.*

🕐 *45 minutes.*

Previous skills/knowledge needed

The children should know the names of the parts of a flowering plant.

Preparation

Visit your chosen survey area to make sure it provides an adequate variety of plant life for the children to find and examine. (Check first which plants are protected by law. As a general rule plants should not be removed from their natural environment.) Make a note of all the plants available for study. An adult helper can be useful for this activity.

Resources needed

Copies of the photocopiable sheet on page 126, pencils, clipboards, an accessible survey area with a range of plants.

Language to be introduced

Petal, flower, stem, leaves, root, environment.

What to do

Explain to the children that they are going for a walk around the school to look for different kinds of plants. Show them the photocopiable sheet, and explain how and where they are going to record the plants they find.

Take the children outside and draw their attention to the trees, shrubs, grasses, mosses and flowers. Some pupils will be happy to notice and talk about the plants they can see. Suggest they make drawings, and encourage them to pay particular attention to the shape and colour of the leaves and flowers on each plant.

Encourage the children to tell you other things about the plants such as:

▲ Which is the tallest/shortest?

▲ Which have the most leaves?

▲ Are they growing in damp/dry, sunny/shady places?

▲ Are there lots of the same plant growing together or is there just one?

Certain flowers such as dandelions, buttercups and daisies, can be collected and taken back to the classroom to be drawn in greater detail.

Suggestion(s) for extension

Draw the children's attention to the relationship between the types and features of plants and the habitats in which they are found.

Suggestion(s) for support

Younger and less able children may be happier to draw the plants they find on blank sheets of paper.

Collate the information from the children's drawings and record it on a large group recording chart. An enlargement of the photocopiable sheet on page 126 can be used for this.

Assessment opportunities

Note the children who are able to name common plants, those who notice specific features and those who are able to give simple reasons as to why they were found where they were.

Display ideas

Make a collage picture of the survey area to display with the children's drawings and paintings.

Aspects of the Science PoS covered

Experimental and Investigative Science – 2b, 2c, 3a, 3c, 3d.

Reference to photocopiable sheet

The photocopiable sheet on page 126 is a collection sheet on which you can enter as much, or as little, information about plants as seems appropriate.

ANIMALS AT SCHOOL

Different animals are found in the school environment.

†† *Class activity.*

🕐 *40 minutes.*

⚠ *Children should be reminded to treat animals with care. Their attention should be drawn to the feelings and needs of the 'captured' animals.*

Previous skills/knowledge needed

None required.

Preparation

Visit the chosen environment to make sure it will provide enough animal life for study and is safe for the children. You

their attention on the habitat and features of the animals. The children can then draw and paint the animal of their choice.

Suggestion(s) for extension
Dig up a small piece of turf from the edge of the school field (or a parent's garden) and take it back to the classroom. Place this on a large piece of polythene on a table and wearing gloves, pull it apart. Using magnifying lenses and magnispectors, list the animal life found in the soil. Carefully put some small creatures in a magnispector or under a microscope and allow every child to have a look. Invite each member of the group to notice something different about the animal – possibly its size, body segments, hairs, eyes, mouth or the way it moves. Replace the animal in the soil after only a few minutes. Repeat with other small creatures.

Suggestion(s) for support
Some children will need to work as part of a very small group, with adult help. It is a good idea to recruit an extra adult to help supervise this activity.

Assessment opportunities
Some children will tell you the names of the animals, others the animal groups they belong to, and some may give reasons why certain kinds of animals were found.

Opportunities for IT
Children might be introduced to simple CD-ROM encyclopaedias which they can use to look for more information on animals they find. Some have recorded sound to describe the animals or minibeasts and include versions of the text for children of different ages.

Display ideas
Display the children's drawings and paintings on a large frieze picture of the local environment.

will need to check which animals are protected by law, such as the common frog. It is better not to remove animals or plants from their natural environment. An extra adult can be helpful for this activity.

Resources needed
Copies of the photocopiable sheet on page 127, pencils, clipboards, polythene sheeting, protective gloves, magnifying lenses, microscope and magnispectors.

Language to be introduced
Hair, feather, shell, damp, dry, under, environment, habitat, magnifying, magnispector, microscope, bigger, smaller, soil.

What to do
Explain to the children that they are going to go out into the school grounds to look for different kinds of animals. The photocopiable sheet on page 127 can be used to record information for discussion after the activity.

During the survey, you should draw the children's attention to how the animal is moving, how many legs it has, whether it has wings, feathers, hair or a shell. Ask questions such as:
▲ Where was the animal found?
▲ Was the area damp or dry, was it under a tree, in the grass or under the ground?
▲ How big is the animal? Is it bigger than your thumbnail?
▲ Was the animal found on its own or in a group?

The animals you are likely to see in the school grounds are birds, insects, cats, snails, spiders, ants, woodlice and worms.

Discuss the animals that the children have found, focusing

Draw pictures of the animals on the back of this sheet.	Name of the animal	Does it: fly?	swim?	walk?	Does it have: a shell?	wings?	feathers?	How many legs does it have?	Did you find it on its own?		

Name Environment: _____

Animal survey

Date _____

Other aspects of the Science PoS covered
Experimental and Investigative Science – 2b, 2c, 3a, 3b, 3c, 3d. Life Processes and Living Things – 1b.

Reference to photocopiable sheet
The photocopiable sheet on page 127 can be used to collect as much, or as little, information about animals as you wish.

PLANTS AND ANIMALS AROUND US

Different plants and animals are found in different environments.

†† *Class or group activity.*

🕐 *45 minutes.*

⚠ *If you are going outside the school environment, you may need some extra adult helpers.*

Previous skills/knowledge needed

The children should have surveyed the plant and animal life *within* the school environment before doing this activity.

Preparation

Visit your chosen environment and make a note of the plant and animal life. The children may need wellington boots. Make a matching game using the photocopiable sheets on pages 128, 129 and 130.

Resources needed

Clipboards, pencils, copies of the photocopiable sheets on pages 128, 129 and 130, sheets of paper, a camera.

What to do

Explain to the children that they are going to the park/pond/beach to look for plants and animals. Explain where and how they are to record what they find.

Take the children to the chosen environment and draw their attention to the trees, shrubs, grasses, flowers, birds, insects and other plant and animal life.

Very young children will be satisfied to notice and talk about the plants and animals around them. Ask the children what plants and animals they can see.

▲ Which plant is the tallest/shortest?

▲ Which flower has the most petals?

▲ Where is that plant? Is it in a shady/dry/damp place?

▲ Where are the animals? Are they under a tree, under the ground, on their own, in groups?

(The more able children will be able to make a record and drawings of their findings. The photocopiable sheets on pages 126 and 127 may be useful for this.)

When you get back into the classroom, spend some time talking about the plants and animals you found. Compare them with the plants and animals that were found in the school environment:

▲ Which plants and animals did you find in both places?

▲ Which plants and animals did you find in only one place?

▲ Why do you think this was?

List, in groups, the plants and animals found in both environments and those found in only one environment.

Suggestion(s) for extension

Using the information collected, make comparisons of habitat and conditions for life. Use secondary sources to research and make comparisons of plant and animal life in other environments.

Suggestion(s) for support

Children with limited drawing skills will be happy for you to photograph the things they find. The photographs can then be used for identification and discussion purposes. If you wish, you can make brief notes of the children's oral responses as evidence of knowledge and understanding.

Assessment opportunities

Make a note of the children who realised that some plants and animals are found in lots of different environments while others are found only in certain environments because of the differences in habitat.

Opportunities for IT

More able readers might be able to use simple CD-ROMS to research extra information about animals and other habitats.

Display ideas

Ask the children to make drawings and paintings of the plants and animals they found. These can be displayed on a background frieze of the environments visited.

Other aspects of the Science PoS covered

Experimental and Investigative Science – 3b, 3c, 3d, 3f.

SCIENCE

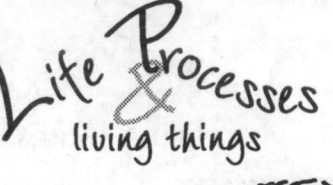
Reference to photocopiable sheets

The photocopiable sheets on pages 128, 129 and 130 contain pictures of two different environments, plants and animals. The plants and animals should be cut out and glued around the relevant environment picture. This can be used as an assessment or recording sheet.

SNAILS

Animals move, feed and grow.
†† *Whole class in groups.*
🕐 *All day.*
⚠ *Explain to the children that they must handle all animals with care. Return all animals to their original habitat once the lesson is completed.*

Previous skills/knowledge needed

Remind the children that all living things should be treated and handled with a lot of care.

Preparation

A damp morning in late spring or early summer is the best time to find a large number and variety of snails. You will usually find them on the underside of leaves and in the undergrowth of hedges, bushes and shrubs, so select a

collecting area with these features. Investigate the collecting area to ensure it contains a variety of snail types and sizes to collect. The children may need wellington boots if the collecting area is muddy.

Resources needed

Plastic trays or ice-cream tubs for collecting snails, aquarium or similar for observing snails (an empty sweet jar will do), suitable foliage from the habitat, rigid transparent plastic sheet, magnifying lenses, a tape recorder and blank tape.

Language to be introduced

Snail, habitat, damp, moist, dry, wet, grass, moss, leaves, undergrowth.

What to do

Gather the children together and explain that they are going to look for snails. Tell them that they will also need to collect some foliage from the area where the snails are found.

Remind them to handle the snails with care and sensitivity so that they are not caused any distress, and advise them not to collect *too* much of the foliage so as not to destroy the natural habitat. At the collecting area, discuss the snails' habitats and living conditions with the children.

▲ What do you notice about the leaves/grass/moss that you have collected?
▲ What colour are they?
▲ Are they dry/damp/wet?
▲ How many snails can you see?
▲ Are the snails on or off the ground?

Carefully collect the snails and place them and some foliage in the collecting tray or container and return to the classroom. Transfer the foliage and snails to the aquarium, then allow the children to observe the snails for a moment and respond to what they notice. Set up a tape recorder near the group to record the children's responses. You will probably find that the children are very excited. Draw the children's attention to the aquarium. Is it similar to the habitat where the snails were found? Encourage them to comment on colour, shape, size, movement and feeding. Compare two snails of the same species:

42

where the snails were found, how they moved and fed and detailed descriptions can be written.

Suggestion(s) for support
Some children may need help with suggestions of what to write about.

Assessment opportunities
From the activity, some children will be able to deduce that snails move, feed and grow. Others will form the hypothesis that all animals move, feed and grow. They should then be encouraged to investigate this further. Some children will use hand magnifiers to observe the movement and feeding of the snails.

Opportunities for IT
Children could record the snail activities (such as moving, still, feeding) during the day using a graphing package. The results for individual snails could be printed out in block graphs or pie charts, and comparisons made between different snails.

Children could use a word processor to write about their viewing period. These could be printed out together to form a running commentary. Reports on where the snails were found and detailed descriptions of the snails themselves could also be word processed for a class display.

Display ideas
Display the children's drawings, paintings and accounts inside a huge snail outline.

Other aspects of the Science PoS covered
Experimental and Investigative Science – 2a.

▲ Are they the same size?

▲ How do we know that the snails grow?

Place a snail on a transparent rigid sheet and let the children watch as the snail moves across it. If the snail is reluctant to move, a small piece of banana, placed at a distance, often provides encouragement. Watch the snail's progress from above and below the sheet. Some children may suggest using hand magnifiers to observe the movements more closely. Can the children explain how the snail moves? Place a leaf from the snail's natural habitat on the sheet and watch as the snail feeds.

▲ Can the children see the snail's mouth?

▲ How does the snail feed?

Record the children's responses.

Throughout the day, groups of children could take it in turns to observe a different snail closely for ten minutes. Ask the children to record what the snail does for most of each minute. Possible observations are staying still, moving and feeding. You may wish to collate the information collected from each group and display it pictorially or graphically. (You could count up all the 'feeding' minutes and build a tower with a matching number of Multilink cubes, then repeat this for 'moving' and 'staying still'. These towers can then be compared and transferred into graphical form to find out how the snails spent their day.) The information collected can later be analysed so that pupils can draw their own conclusions.

At the end of the day, take the children back to the collecting area to return the snails to their natural habitat. Be sure to explain why it is necessary to do this.

Suggestion(s) for extension
Some children will be able to use hand magnifiers to support close observational drawings. Reports of

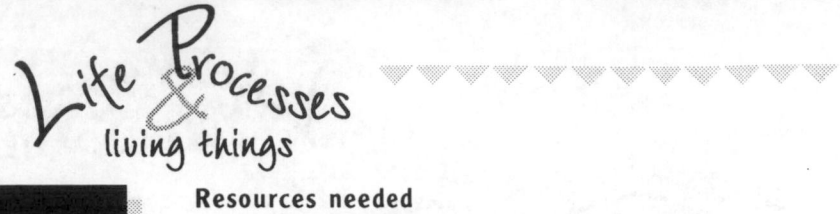

ALIVE OR NOT?

Some things have never been alive.

✝✝ *Group activity.*

🕐 *30 minutes.*

Previous skills/knowledge needed

The children should have completed activities to find out that animals (including humans) move, feed, grow, use their senses and reproduce.

Preparation

Make a collection of pictures of living things and things which have never been alive, such as animals, humans, furniture, household appliances (including a television), plants, toys, tools, books and food.

Resources needed

A collection of pictures as detailed above, sorting rings, copies of the photocopiable sheet on page 131, cut up, for children to sort, labels.

Language to be introduced

Living, move, grow, alive, dead, reproduce.

What to do

Spread out the pictures in the centre of a circle of children and spend some time discussing with them what they are. Focus the children's attention on the similarities and differences between the pictures. Ask one child to choose a picture, then encourage the other children to find something which has a similarity to the chosen item.

Ask the children to sort the pictures into sets. Initially,

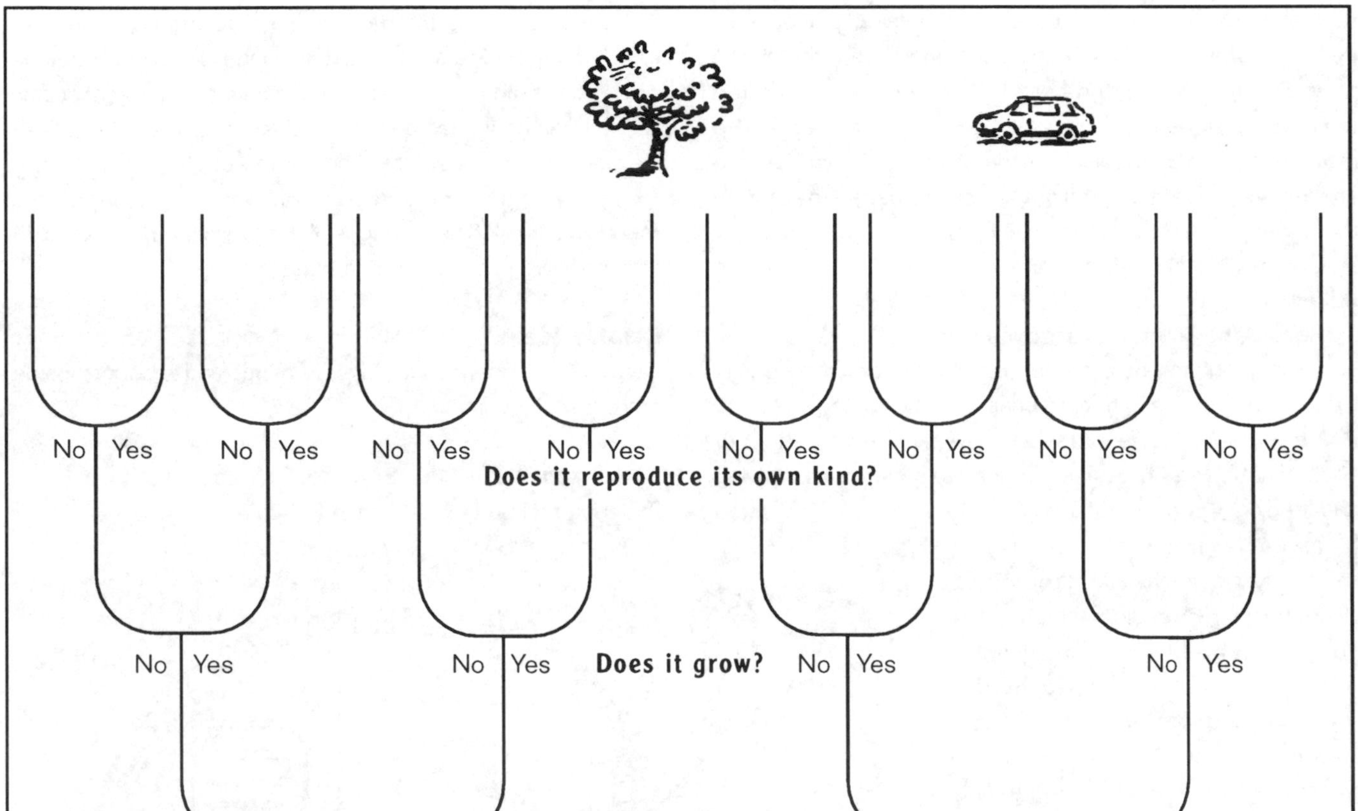

No Yes   No Yes   No Yes   No Yes   No Yes   No Yes   No Yes   No Yes

Does it reproduce its own kind?

No Yes   No Yes   **Does it grow?**   No Yes   No Yes

No Yes   **Does it feed?**   No Yes

No Yes

Does it move?

allow them to decide the criteria for sorting and think of a label for each set.

Ask the children to sort again according to whether the item moves/eats/grows/uses its senses/can reproduce its own kind. You can then ask them to sort the pictures into sets of 'is living' and 'has never been alive'. Ask what they notice about the sets, but be careful not to confuse them by forcing a right answer onto them. At this stage, children should be able to recognise that some things are living and others are not. It is not important if they do not know why.

Depending on the children's experience of sorting, you can record this activity in pictures, using Venn or Carroll diagrams (use the photocopiable sheets on pages 114 and 116).

Name _____ Living or not Date _____

Suggestion(s) for extension
More able children can be introduced to a simple decision tree using the same sorting criteria as questions for simple classification. They can then make a list of things that they think are alive and things that have never been alive.

Suggestion(s) for support
Not all children will be able to tell you the differences between things that are living and things that have never been alive. Young children find this concept very difficult – to them a television is alive because it has to be turned on, it eats electricity and has moving pictures. It is far better to abandon questioning to avoid confusion and wait until the children are ready to work out the differences for themselves.

Assessment opportunities
Make a note of those children who have grasped this difficult concept.

Display ideas
Display some of the pictures with the children's charts and diagrams.

Other aspects of the Science PoS covered
Life Processes and Living Things – 1b.

Reference to photocopiable sheet
The photocopiable sheet on page 131 provides a set of pictures of inanimate objects, animals and plants for sorting. These should be cut out and mounted onto card before using. You could also cover, or spray, them, to avoid damage when being handled.

ARE PEOPLE AND ANIMALS ALIKE?

People and animals have similarities and differences.
†† Group activity.
🕐 30 minutes.

Previous skills/knowledge needed
None required.

Preparation
Make a collection of pictures of animals and people.

Resources needed
A collection of pictures, sorting rings, copies of the photocopiable sheet on page 116, large sheets of paper, adhesive.

Language to be introduced
Similar, the same, different.

What to do
Spread the pictures out in the centre of a group of children. Spend some time discussing the animals and people in the pictures. Ask the children:
▲ What do all the animals and people have?
▲ What do some animals have that people don't?
▲ What do some animals have that other animals don't?

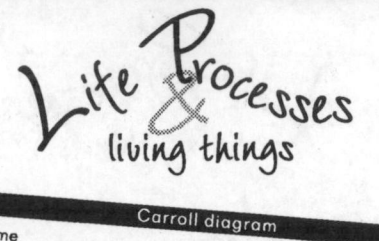

▲ What do people have that animals don't?

▲ Are some animals different and some the same?

▲ Do all the animals have legs?

Encourage the children to ask questions which will sort the animals into groups of similarities and differences. Label the sets they have made.

Sort the pictures into 'have' or 'have not' groups, recording the classifications on Carroll diagrams (see page 116). Examples of groupings are 'have' or 'have not':

▲ feathers

▲ legs

▲ hair

▲ tail

▲ wings

▲ hands.

Make a list of things that humans and animals have in common and a list of things that are different.

Carroll diagram

Name _____

Date _____

Suggestion(s) for extension

Extend the 'have'/'have not' criteria to more refined differences and similarities such as lays eggs, webbed feet, position of eyes. The children may be able to classify using a simple decision tree.

Suggestion(s) for support

It may be necessary to have several sets of pictures so that the children can stick the groupings onto large sheets of paper as they sort them.

Assessment opportunities

Most children will be able to tell you that animals are different from people and give you simple reasons. This activity will allow you to develop the children's observations to specific criteria and to assess which children are ready for more detailed classification activities.

Opportunities for IT

Some children might be able to transfer their decision tree on to a computer branching database.

Display ideas

Display the recordings the children have made with the questions they have raised. Display the list you have made of things that animals and humans have in common and how they are different. Encourage the children to add to the list.

Other aspects of the Science PoS covered

Experimental and Investigative Science – 2b, 2c, 3a, 3b, 3c, 3d.

Reference to photocopiable sheet

The photocopiable sheet on page 116 provides a Carroll diagram outline for children to fill in.

Materials & their properties

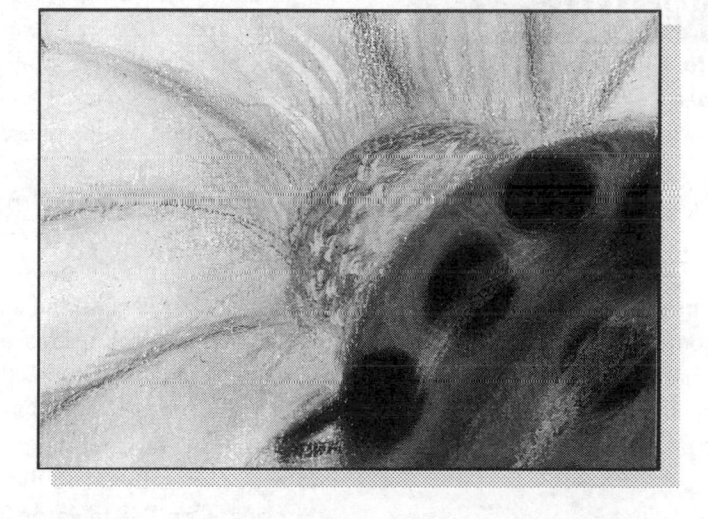

This section of the book contains activities on grouping materials and changing materials. The lessons use everyday items to develop the children's understanding of the nature of materials and their properties through a series of practical activities which include sorting, model-making and cookery.

The learning potential of many lessons can be increased if both the raw and processed versions of a material are available for the children to see and handle. Explore the possibility of obtaining raw material samples of wool, various metals and wood.

The collections of materials needed in many activities can be made more varied and interesting if they are built up over a long time. Create collections of buttons, textiles, rocks, wood and paper for use in science, and store them for repeated use. Other resources used in the lessons include:

▲ cooking facilities;
▲ water tray;
▲ clay.

Language to be introduced

Hard, soft, fluffy, rough, smooth, rigid, velvety, shiny, dull, reflecting, bright, blunt, sharp, hot, cold, slippery, dry, coarse, round, powdery, heavy, light, colour, tinkling, bang, knock.

What to do

Sit the children in a ring around the collection of materials. Ask each child to choose one item from the collection to explore. Invite the children to tell you something about their item:

▲ What does it feel like?
▲ What does it look like?
▲ What colour is it?
▲ Does it make a sound?

Can they tell you what it is made from? If not, encourage the pupils to think up descriptive names for the material, such as 'bendy, soft, grey stuff'. This will offer an opportunity to develop the children's language. Write the children's suggestions and the actual name of the material on a large sheet of paper to use in the next part of the activity.

Next, play a game of 'Materials snap'. Hold up an item from the collection. Ask the children to hold up their item and shout 'Snap' if it matches. Ask them:

▲ Why did you shout 'Snap'?
▲ In what ways are these things the same?
▲ Are they shiny/rough/reflective/white and so on?

Tap a metal, plastic or wooden object with a metal or wooden stick. Discuss the sound. Can the children find another object which makes a similar sound? Hold up the item and shout 'Snap' if they think it does.

Continue the game until you are satisfied the children can recognise and name simple properties of texture, sound and appearance by using their senses. Choose one item and place it on the table or floor, possibly on a sheet of paper. Ask the children to find something else which is similar and place it next to the first item. Join the two items with a double-sided arrow labelled 'They are both ....' (add the matching property).

The game can be repeated with the children choosing an item which is in some way different from the first item. These items can then be labelled with a double-sided arrow which reads 'They are different because ....'.

You may wish to collate the information on a chart using the photocopiable sheet on page 132.

KNOCK --- ON WOOD

We can use our senses to find similarities and differences between materials.

†† *Class or group of eight to ten children.*

🕐 *40 minutes.*

⚠ *Ensure the materials you choose are safe to handle and free from sharp edges.*

Previous skills/knowledge needed

The children will gain more from this activity if they have previous experience of exploring using their senses (see the activities on the senses in the chapter on 'Life Processes and Living Things' pages 14–20).

Preparation

Make a collection of raw materials and/or items manufactured from them. Include examples of wood, textiles, plastic, metal, paper and rock. The collection can be made as a previous teaching activity, carried out by the teacher or by the children themselves.

Resources needed

A collection of materials (as detailed above), felt-tipped pens, an area of table or floor, or a large sheet of paper, paper arrows.

they are both smooth and rigid — sheet metal

they are both hard — Plastic box

they are both rough — tree bark — rock

Suggestion(s) for extension

Ask the children to compare two materials on the collation chart (page 132).

▲ Can they list at least three things which are the same about them?

▲ Can they list at least three things that are different about them?

Encourage them to ask each other questions:

▲ Which materials are hard/rough/shiny?

▲ Which materials are not?

The children may wish to record their findings using the photocopiable sheet on page 133.

Suggestion(s) for support

Some children will not have the appropriate language to describe what they can feel and see. Continue to play the game in smaller groups, introducing the similarities and differences yourself.

Choose one item, pass it around the children and ask them to feel how smooth it is, to see how shiny it is, and so on. Ask them to find another item which is similar (feels smooth) or one which is different (feels rough). Their discoveries can be recorded by gluing small pieces of the material on to the photocopiable sheet on page 49.

Continue until you are satisfied the children have acquired the language necessary to determine the similarities and differences of materials.

Assessment opportunities

Make a note of the children who need help to identify the similarities and differences of the materials and give them more experience of this activity.

The more able children will notice more obscure things about the materials related to their uses, such as 'these are all waterproof', 'these keep us warm'. These children can be encouraged to investigate their hypotheses further.

Opportunities for IT

Younger children could record their work using a concept keyboard linked to a word processor. The concept keyboard could have pictures of the various materials and then a list of words which pupils can match to the relevant material (perhaps a picture of metal and the word 'shiny'). This would appear on the screen as 'The metal is shiny'. Other picture vocabulary combinations could be used according to the objects selected and the age and ability of the children. This work introduces pupils to other keyboards, and gives computer access to children with limited writing skills.

Similar work could be undertaken using framework software like *My World* which enables children to link pictures and words on the screen, or to add their own text. A growing number of prepared files are available commercially.

Children could discuss where they have seen similar keyboards used outside school (in cafes and restaurants such as McDonald's). Ask them to suggest reasons (easier to keep clean, saves time, prevents mistakes over prices.)

Display ideas

Display the collection of materials on a display board and table or cupboard top with the children's questions, teacher's questions and collation sheets.

The materials can be labelled with their actual properties and descriptions of them by the children.

Other aspects of the Science PoS covered

Materials and their Properties – 1b.
Experimental and Investigative Science – 2a, 3c.

Reference to photocopiable sheets

The photocopiable sheet on page 132 is a recording sheet which allows the children to classify materials, according to their properties, at a simple level, listing the materials which are rough, smooth, shiny, dull, hard, soft. The sheet can easily be adapted to record other properties if you wish.

The photocopiable sheet on page 133 is designed to extend the children's thinking by identifying specific properties of materials. The completed sheet will contain lists of properties of metal, rock, plastic, wood, paper and textiles. This sheet can be completed immediately after the activity or used as an assessment sheet at a later date.

Analyse the completed sheets in small groups and, from the collected information, ask the children to write simple descriptions of each material, along the lines of 'metal is shiny, smooth, hard and can be shaped'.

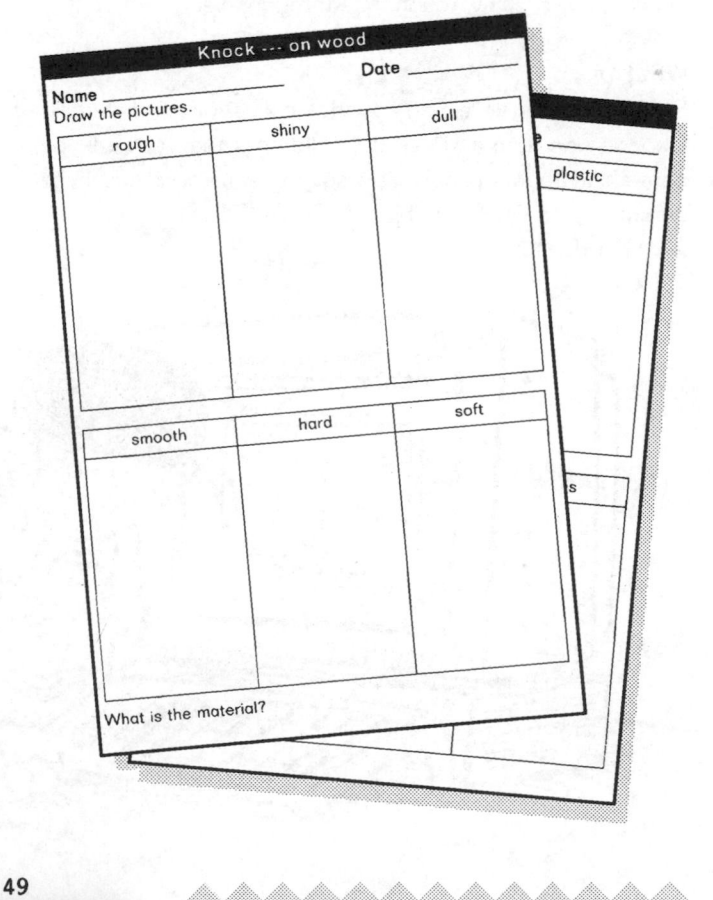

I CAN SEE RIGHT THROUGH

To be able to sort materials into groups according to properties of texture, appearance and transparency.

† *Groups of eight to ten children.*

⏱ *40 minutes.*

⚠ *Remind the children about the need to handle glass with care and the procedure to follow if a glass is broken accidentally. Cling film and polythene are also dangerous and should never be put near noses and mouths. If in doubt, leave them out!*

Previous skills/knowledge needed

The children should have the appropriate language for describing the properties of texture and appearance of materials (see the lesson 'Knock --- on wood' on page 48).

Preparation

Make a collection of raw materials and/or objects made from them. These should include wood, plastics, textiles, paper, metal and rock. Also include transparent items, such as glass, clear plastic lids and drinks bottles (some of which can be filled with water), Cellophane, Sellotape, cling film, ice, OHP film, coloured acetate.

Resources needed

A collection of materials, set rings, labels, felt-tipped pen.

Language to be introduced

Transparent, texture, appearance, properties, stretch, squash, twist, shiny, rough, see-through, clear.

What to do

Sit the children in a ring round a collection of materials. Choose one item and ask the children if they can tell you something about the object. Pass the item around and invite comments on what the object feels like.

▲ What does it look like?

▲ What does it sound like if we tap it?

▲ What material is it made from?

▲ Is it big?

▲ Can it be squashed, stretched or twisted?

Choose one of the suggested descriptive words, such as shiny, rough or squashy, and ask the children to find another item which matches that description. Place both items in a set ring and label the set. Continue to sort the items into sets according to the properties of texture and appearance. The more able children and those with previous sorting experience will probably be able to do this without much help.

When the materials have been sorted according to the properties of texture and appearance, draw the children's attention (if they have not already noticed) to the fact that you can see through some items and not others; that some items are clear or transparent. Allow the children to look through these items and respond to what they see. Ask them to put all the items which are transparent into one set and all the objects which are not in another set. Label the sets 'Can see through – transparent' and 'Cannot see through – not transparent'. Ask the children if they notice anything about the materials in both sets. Some children may be able to tell you that the transparent items are made of glass, plastic, textiles or paper and those that are not transparent are made of these same materials plus wood, rock and metal.

Ask the children to record the sets they have made.

Suggestion(s) for extension

Develop the children's sorting skills by using them to sort the materials according to properties, such as transparency

SCIENCE

and smoothness. The children will realise that some items can belong to both sets. Give them a chance to work out for themselves how they can put the items into both sets. If the children cannot do this, teach them the recording strategy of overlapping sets.

Suggestion(s) for support
Some children will need to glue samples of materials directly on to large sheets of paper or set up a 3-D display of the sets they have made.

Assessment opportunities
Make a note of the children who are able to sort the materials unaided according to texture, appearance and transparency. Some will also sort them according to less obvious properties related to their uses, such as strong, waterproof, provides warmth, and so on. Encourage these pupils to investigate their hypotheses if you wish.

Opportunities for IT
Younger children could record their work using a concept keyboard linked to a word processor. The concept keyboard could have pictures of the various materials and then a list of appropriate words for children to match to the relevant material. So a picture of cling film could be linked to the words transparent, twist, clear and could be linked to make the sentence 'Cling film is clear'. Different overlays could be created to cater for differing age and ability. This activity gives children opportunities to use a wider range of keyboards.

Similar work could be undertaken using framework software like *My World*. This gives children the opportunity to link pictures and words on screen, or to add their own text. A growing number of prepared files are available commercially.

Children could discuss where such keyboards are used outside school (in cafes and restaurants such as McDonald's). They could try to suggest reasons (easier to keep clean, saves time, prevents mistakes over prices).

Display ideas
Set up an interactive display in the classroom to allow the children to continue this activity during the week. Ask them to sort the materials using a different criteria each day.

Other aspects of the Science PoS covered
Experimental and Investigative Science – 2a, 3c.
Materials and their Properties – 1b.

MAGNETIC AND NON-MAGNETIC MATERIALS

To know that some materials are magnetic and others are non-magnetic.
†† *Group activity.*
🕐 *20 minutes.*

Previous skills/knowledge needed
None required.

Preparation
Make a collection of materials, including a variety of metals, for the extension activity. Some of the objects should be light enough to be lifted by the magnets you are using. Do not use plastic-covered metals such as paper-clips or electrical wire for the main activity. Young children may not realise that there is metal inside and misconceptions can easily occur. Adjust the photocopiable sheet on page 121.

Resources needed
A collection of materials, enough magnets for the children to have one each, paper, pencils, adhesive, a large sheet of paper for recording. Take copies of the adjusted photocopiable sheet.

Language to be introduced
Attract, magnetic, non-magnetic, repel, push away, pull together.

What to do
Put the collection of materials in the centre of a table. Give each child in the group a magnet and tell them its name. Ask if anyone knows what a magnet does and, if so, invite them to show the group. Allow the children to play with the magnets for about five minutes to explore and make discoveries about the items in the collection. Most will also try their magnet on another magnet. At the end of this short session, ask the children if they have discovered anything their magnet can do. You may get a variety of responses: some pupils will say that they can pick up some of the items, others may mention that the magnet sticks to some of them but does not stick to others.

Direct their attention to the types of materials from which the objects in the collection are made. Ask the children what they notice when they put the magnet next to the paper-clip, teaspoon, soft drinks can, button, pencil, and so on.

Explain that when something sticks to the magnet we say the material is attracted to the magnet or is 'magnetic'.

Suggestion(s) for extension
The children who notice that the objects attracted to their magnet are made from metal could explore a collection of

metal objects. Include aluminium foil, coins, paper-clips, brass pins, cans, spoons, and so on. Ask the children what they think will happen if they put their magnets next to these items. They will probably say the magnet will stick to all of them because they are all made of metal! Ask the children to use their magnets to find out if they are all magnetic. They can then record their findings on an adjusted copy of the photocopiable sheet on page 121.

Suggestion(s) for support
The photocopiable sheet on page 121 has two columns. These can be labelled 'Magnetic' (✓) and 'Non-magnetic' (✗). The (✓) and (✗) will help non-readers know which column is which. Using the magnets, the children can find out which materials are magnetic and which are not and glue samples or pictures of each material on to the chart.

Assessment opportunities
Make a note of the children who understand that 'magnetic' means something which is attracted to a magnet. It may be appropriate for these children to complete the extension activity. Those who complete the extension activity may be able to conclude that magnetic materials are usually metal, but that not all metals are magnetic.

Opportunities for IT
Younger children could record their work using a concept keyboard linked to a word processor. The concept keyboard could have pictures of the various materials and the words 'magnetic' and 'non-magnetic' – children can then link the material to the appropriate word and print out their answers. This could be used as a way of assessing children's understanding of the work covered. Different overlays could be created to cover a range of ages and abilities. This activity gives children opportunities to use a wider range of keyboards. Older or more able children could use a word processor for the same activity.

Ask children where they have seen similar keyboards used outside school (in restaurants such as McDonald's). Can

they suggest reasons why they are used (easier to keep clean, saves time, prevents mistakes over prices)?

Display ideas
Display the children's completed charts with the collection of materials.

Other aspects of the Science PoS covered
Experimental and Investigative Science – 3d.

Reference to photocopiable sheets
The photocopiable sheet on page 121 can be used for this activity. Photocopy one sheet and replace the words 'healthy/not healthy' with 'magnetic/not magnetic' before photocopying the required number. The sheet will provide evidence of the children's knowledge of magnetic and non-magnetic materials.

Name _____
Date _____
Healthy eating
Draw pictures of some foods which are healthy and some which are not healthy.

healthy (✓)	not healthy (✗)

NAMING MATERIALS

To be able to identify wood, textiles, plastic, rock, paper and metal.

†† *Class activity.*

🕐 *20 minutes.*

Previous skills/knowledge needed

The children should have experience of sorting a collection of materials using their senses (see the lesson 'Knock --- on wood' on page 18).

Preparation

Make sure there are a number of different items in the classroom which are safe for the children to handle. Put a small sticker on the things you want them to find and play a game of 'Hunt the material', secure in the knowledge that all the items will be safe to handle. Set aside an area for displaying the collected items.

Resources needed

One item made of each of the following materials: metal, plastic, paper, textiles, rock and wood, labels, stickers.

Language to be introduced

Rock, paper, textiles, wood, plastic, metal, soft, rough, stretchy, hard, smooth, shiny, transparent, see-through, magnetic, bendy, fluffy, slippery, rigid, heavy, light, dull, reflective.

What to do

Gather the children together and pass round the items made of wood, metal, paper, plastic, textiles and rock for the children to feel and look at. Ask the children what materials the items are made from. How do they know? Repeat the reasons they give so that all of the children in the group can hear.

Retrieve the items, then tap each one in turn with a metal beater. After each tap ask the children to describe the sound they hear. Can they tell what the material is by listening? Ask the children to close their eyes and tap one of the items again. Ask them if they can tell you which one you tapped. Tap the item they suggest to check if it is the correct one.

Lay out the items in the display area. Write on a label the name of the material from which each item is made, and display this clearly.

Next, explain that you want the children to look for, and collect, items made from wood, metal, textiles, rock, paper and plastic and group them together to form a large display of materials. Show them where to put their collected items.

Watch the children carefully to make sure they have correctly identified the material before they display their item. Ask each child for the name of the material they have collected.

▲ How do they know which material it is?
▲ What does it look like, feel like, sound like if tapped?
▲ Is it transparent, magnetic, and so on?

Send the children to look for an item made from a different material. When the collection is made, the children can paint pictures of other items they could add to the collection but which are too heavy to carry. Follow-up discussions and sorting of the collection should determine which materials are found naturally in the environment and which materials are man-made.

Suggestion(s) for extension

Sort and label one part of the collection into subsets of natural and man-made.

Suggestion(s) for support

Very young children will need to do this activity over a number of weeks and concentrate on collecting one material at a time for display.

Assessment opportunities

Make a note of the children who can/cannot recognise and name the materials. Those who cannot should be given further experience of sorting materials using their senses.

Opportunities for IT

The number of items in each of the material columns could be added up to provide a number which could be plotted using graphing software. Pupils could discuss what the graph shows in terms of the most-used or least-used material, then try to decide why.

Children could also discuss with the teacher the benefits of using the computer for this sort of work.

Display ideas

Display the collection with the children's paintings either as one display or several displays around the room.

Other aspects of the Science PoS covered

Experimental and Investigative Science – 2a.

MATERIALS WITH MANY USES

Some materials have many different uses.
Groups of six to eight children.
30 minutes.

Previous skills/knowledge needed

The children should be able to identify these materials: wood, plastic, paper, textiles, glass and metal.

Preparation

Make a collection of items made from *one* of the materials mentioned above. Be sure to include examples of the various uses of the material chosen, such as plastic containers, toys, book covers, chair seats. Make enough copies of the photocopiable sheet on page 134 for each child to have one.

Resources needed

A collection of your chosen material, copies of the photocopiable sheet on page 134, clipboards, pencils, an additional adult helper (if the children will be leaving the classroom).

Language to be introduced

Wood, plastic, metal, paper, textiles, glass.

What to do

Place your chosen collection in the centre of a group of children. Ask the children to tell you what the items are used for, such as furniture, book covering, footwear, containers, and so on. Make a note of the variety of uses of your chosen material.

Ask the children if they can see another material in the classroom which has lots of uses:
▲ What are its uses?
▲ Can they think of any other uses for this material?
▲ Why do they think this material was chosen for each particular job?

Ask the children if they can see where glass is used in the classroom:
▲ How many different ways is it used?
▲ Where in the classroom is it used?

Show the children the photocopiable sheet. Explain that they will be going for a walk around the school looking for all the different uses of wood, plastic, metal, paper, textiles and glass. Show them where they are to record their findings. Some children may wish to record with pictures, some with words. Send the children with an adult to look for the different uses. When they return, ask them what they found.
▲ How many different ways is plastic used?
▲ Which material had the most, and the least uses?

Suggestion(s) for extension

More able children may be able to relate the properties of the materials to their uses and try to make generalisations from the information gathered, such as:
▲ Metal is used for holding things in place – window frames, containers and coat pegs.
▲ Wood is used for furniture, doors and PE benches.
▲ Plastic is used for containers, furniture, book coverings and toys.

Encourage the children to give reasons *why* the materials are used to make these items.

SCIENCE

Suggestion(s) for support

Very young children will not be able to cope with collecting more than one material at a time. They should work in groups, with each group looking for items made of one particular material. The groups can report back to each other at the end of the activity.

The worksheet can be simplified for poor readers by adding pictogram characters to, or highlighting with colour, the initial letter of each material's name. This will help children identify the correct column when recording the collected items.

Assessment opportunities

Make a note of the children who can/cannot identify the same materials in different situations.

Display ideas

Collate the children's findings on to a large wall chart and display it alongside the children's drawings and paintings.

Other aspects of the Science PoS covered

Experimental and Investigative Science – 2a, 2b, 2c, 3a, 3c, 3d.

Reference to photocopiable sheet

The photocopiable sheet on page 134 is a survey sheet on which the children can record the different items made of the materials explored in this bank of lessons. It can also be used as an assessment sheet to provide evidence of the children's ability to identify materials.

MATERIALS WITH SPECIAL USES

Some materials have specific uses.
†† *Group activity.*
🕐 *30 minutes.*

Previous skills/knowledge needed

The children should have covered the work included in the lessons on identifying and naming common materials (pages 48–54) and understand the main properties, including transparency, appearance and texture.

Preparation

Select a number of items the children have identified on their materials survey sheet for the activity 'Materials with many uses' (page 54). Prepare a series of questions to ask the children which will encourage them to think about why certain materials are used for specific purposes such as glass for windows, plastic for wellingtons, metal for saucepans, cotton/polyester for sweatshirts.

Resources needed

A window in the classroom, a saucepan with a plastic or wooden handle, a sweatshirt, plastic wellington boots, a large sheet of paper to record the children's suggestions, copies of the photocopiable sheets on pages 135 and 136.

Language to be introduced

Waterproof, strong, warm, melts, heat, light, cold, soft, bendy, flexible, stretchy, hard, hardwearing, heavy, pretty, bright, colourful, keeps things warm, easy to clean, dries quickly, absorbent, non-slip, smooth, transparent.

What to do

Tell the children that certain materials are chosen for particular things because they have a special job to do. Then ask them to suggest why glass is used in windows. They may say so that they can look through it; so that they can look out; to keep out the rain or wind or cold; to let light in; to keep out burglars, and so on. If nobody suggests it is to let light through, ask them if it would be a good idea to use wood or metal for windows instead of glass. They will then realise that it would be dark inside, and they wouldn't be able to see where they were going and would bump into things; nor would they be able to see out. Emphasise that glass is used because it is transparent. It lets light come through so that we can see indoors, it lets us see out and it also keeps out the wind, rain and cold.

Next, hold up a wellington boot. Ask the children when and why they wear wellingtons.
▲ Can they think of a reason why they are made of plastic?
▲ Why aren't they made of paper, wood or metal?

Record the children's responses on a large sheet of paper. Now hold up the saucepan.

▲ Why is it made of metal?

▲ Why isn't it made of plastic or wood?

▲ But why is the handle plastic or wood?

▲ Why isn't the handle made of metal?

Hold up the sweatshirt. Why and when do we wear sweatshirts? Talk to the children about what they wear when the weather is hot.

▲ Are the clothes made of thick or thin material?

▲ How many layers of clothing do they wear?

▲ What do they wear when the weather is cold?

▲ Are the clothes thick or thin?

▲ How many layers of clothing do they wear then?

▲ What do they notice about the number of clothes they wear in hot and cold weather?

▲ How are the materials different?

▲ Are they different colours?

▲ Why do we wear thicker materials when it is cold?

Let the children have copies of the photocopiable sheet on page 136 to record their ideas.

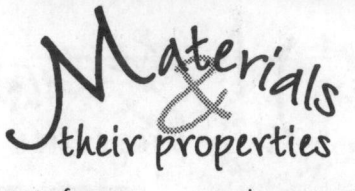

Suggestion(s) for extension

The more able pupils may wish to investigate which materials are waterproof and discuss whether a different material would be suitable for wellington boots. The 'Investigations' chapter has a lesson on absorbency which you may wish to use (page 97).

Suggestion(s) for support

Some children should only explore one material. They could possibly test their own wellingtons. Take them out when there are lots of puddles on the playground. Let them splash about, then inspect their socks on return to the classroom. Why are they still dry?

Assessment opportunities

Watch the children carefully and make a note of who can give reasons why wellingtons are made of plastic and not of wood, paper, etc. Which children are able to draw conclusions about why certain materials are used for particular purposes? Can they relate the uses to the properties of the materials?

Display ideas

Display a summer outfit and a winter outfit, matching the items using one-to-one correspondence and noting the differences in number, thickness and types of material. Add the questions used during the activity and the children's suggestions as to why certain materials are used in particular ways.

Other aspects of the Science PoS covered

Materials and their Properties – 1a, 1b, 1c, 1d.

Reference to photocopiable sheets

The photocopiable sheet on page 135 asks the children to match each sentence to one of the pictures. Note that two sentences apply to the saucepan. This is a useful reinforcement to what has been discussed in the lesson.

The photocopiable sheet on page 136 provides a differentiated task for the less able and asks the children to dress the person in the picture for warm or cold weather, counting the number of items in each instance, and noting the difference. The sheet could be enlarged for children with poor manipulative and fine motor skills. You will need to sit with the children completing this sheet to make sure they really understand the properties of the clothing worn in winter.

SQUASHED BANANA SANDWICHES

Some objects can have their shape changed by squashing.

†† *Whole class, split into groups.*

🕐 *About 20 minutes to make the dough.*

Note: *This activity could take most of the day to complete with groups of children taking turns to cook and prepare the food for eating.*

⚠ *Care should be taken with issues of food hygiene. Consult your school's own documentation for guidance. Each group will need adult supervision while cooking. Young children should be kept away from conventional ovens.*

Previous skills/knowledge needed
None required.

Preparation
Organise additional adult help. If you want to turn the day into an event, such as a Teddy Bears' Picnic, write to parents well in advance telling them what the children should bring with them. Check to see if any children have food allergies or follow specific food customs – this may influence your choice of ingredients. Just before the lesson prepare the work surfaces and take out all necessary cooking utensils, bowls, etc. Choose a warm, clean area in which the dough can prove.

Select and prepare additional classroom activities which will be useful, but which will require the least possible teacher input so that the children will still be busy when not engaged in the cooking or science parts of the activity. The photocopiable sheets on pages 137 and 138 may be useful.

Resources needed
One ripe banana for every two or three children, ingredients for bread making, loaf tins, mixing bowls, forks and bowls to mash bananas, butter or margarine for the sandwiches. Copies of the necessary photocopiable sheets (pages 137 and 138).

Language to be introduced
Dough, squash, squashed, press, push, pull, twist, crush, knead.

What to do
Talk to the children about the format of the day. Set your usual rules for health and safety when dealing with foodstuffs. Pre-heat the oven. *Either* use the additional adult help to supervise the bulk of the class while you get the bread-making started *or* ask your helper to start the bread-making and to call you when the children are ready to knead the dough.

Help the children develop the language of forces as they handle the dough. Talk about pushes, pulls and twists, and look at the way in which the pushing and pulling makes the dough into different shapes. Ask the children:

▲ When you squash the dough are you pushing or pulling?

▲ What happens to the dough when you squash it?

▲ Does it spring back into shape or does it stay as a different shape?

Retain a little dough and cook the rest. Repeat this until all your groups have made their bread.

When the bread has been cooked, and cooled sufficiently to be cut, you can take a slice of the loaf and compare the finished bread with the uncooked dough. Ask the children what happens when bread is squashed and point out that bakers and shop-keepers are very careful how they store and display bread. Customers do not like to buy squashed loaves of bread. Pupils may have noticed that their parents too are careful how they handle bread and try not to crush it in the supermarket trolley or when it is put in the freezer at home.

Ask the children to record what they have done by drawing pictures to show the different stages of the bread-making process. They could then label these, or add captions.

Later in the day, take each group in turn again and prepare the banana sandwich filling. As the children are squashing their bananas ask them to describe what is happening to the shape and consistency of the fruit:

▲ Where has your banana gone?

▲ What have you done to it?

▲ How did you make it look like that?

▲ What is your banana like now?

▲ Have you changed the banana's shape by squashing it?

When all the children have finished making their sandwiches, they can eat them! The photocopiable sheet on page 138 can be filled in once the activity is completed.

Suggestion(s) for extension
It may be possible to introduce the idea of twisting by getting some of the children to produce a plaited loaf.

Ask the more able children to compile a list of foods which we squash or crush before we eat them. Some children may be able to relate the action of chewing to crushing and squashing and to relate this in turn to the preparation and consistency of baby foods. You may wish to choose a group to produce a different style of bread, perhaps an unleavened Indian bread, to show the different types of bread.

Suggestion(s) for support
To reinforce the idea that there are various ways in which we can change the shape of an object, some children could use salt dough to produce model loaves of bread during the day.

Assessment opportunities
Check to see which children can/cannot describe the way in which their actions changed the shape of the dough and the banana.

Opportunities for IT
Children could use a concept keyboard linked to a word processor to sequence the various activities involved in preparing their food. The overlay could contain pictures, or sentences, depending on the age and ability of the children. Alternatively, pupils could write instructions using a word processor, working in pairs or groups, or with the aid of an adult helper, to describe how the food was prepared.

Children could also make their own picnic menus, using a simple word processor and deciding on the size and style of font to be used. A parent or other helper could help children to enter the text at the computer. A standard 'menu' page format could be created in advance giving a border or large font sizes.

Other aspects of the Science PoS covered
Materials and their Properties – 2b.
Physical Processes – 2d.

Display ideas
Display the children's work for the Teddy Bears' Picnic with photographs of the picnic itself.

Reference to photocopiable sheets
Page 137 provides a simple recipe for bread.

The photocopiable sheet on page 138 is a recording sheet which should be completed after the children have finished the activity. Pair a more able child with a less able child or use an adult helper for support. The children should cut out the pictures and paste them on to a piece of paper in the order that they did the activity.

THE BENDY PUPPET

Some objects can be changed in shape by bending.

†† *Individuals, possibly working in differentiated ability groups with additional adult support.*

🕐 *40 minutes.*

⚠ *Be sure to provide adequate tools if you expect the children to cut wire.*

Previous skills/knowledge needed

Individual teachers will need to assess whether the children's previous Design and Technology experience has equipped them to carry out the model-making task.

Preparation

Decide on the style of puppet you wish the children to make. (Either choose just one design or organise your class in ability groups and set the most able a harder modelling task.) Gather together your materials. If the children will need to use tape to stick the model you may wish to collect a number of tape dispensers. Alternatively, consider using masking tape – the children will be able to tear each piece to the required length and it has the added advantage that it can be coloured after use.

Practise making the puppet/s yourself before trying it with the children. In addition to increasing your confidence when carrying out the lesson, this also provides you with an example to show any children who do not understand what the end-product should look like and be able to do.

Resources needed

According to the bendy puppet design you choose to follow you will need:

Puppet 1 Pipe-cleaners for the body (ready cut to the correct size, or whole pipe-cleaners with appropriate cutters, such as good scissors, tin-snips or small electrical wire-cutters), some small pieces of card on which faces can be drawn, adhesive tape, felt-tipped pens.

Puppet 2 Three pieces of A4 paper per child (this can be scrap paper from the office, providing it is not creased), adhesive tape, felt-tipped pens.

Puppet 3 A length of thin garden wire per child with appropriate cutting tools, newspaper, adhesive tape, a simple cloak or tunic design to dress the puppet, felt-tipped pens to draw the detail on the face, illustration of puppets' cloak/tunic which can be made of paper or a light-coloured fabric.

No matter which design you choose you will also need a range of suitable materials which would not be suitable for bendy puppet-making such as lolly sticks, empty plastic bottles, cardboard tubes, and so on.

Language to be introduced

Bend, bendy, flexible joints, push, pull, twist.

What to do

Talk to the children about the way in which their bodies bend:
▲ Where do they bend?
▲ Is every bit of them bendy?
▲ Which bits are bendy?
Encourage them to look at the skin on their knees, elbows and finger joints.
▲ What happens to your skin when you bend your fingers?
▲ Which way do your fingers bend?

Explain to the children that they are going to make a simple puppet which can bend like they can. What sort of material do they think they should use?

Show the collection of materials to the children and discuss their ideas about suitable materials for puppet-making. Keep reminding them that the puppets they are going to make must be able to bend in all the same places as they themselves can bend. Be careful not to dismiss the children's creative ideas at this stage. They may well be able to see ways of creating bendy puppets out of all sorts of rigid materials. This will be particularly likely if they are experienced modellers and have the idea that rigid materials can be hinged (like our bones). If they come up with ideas which include rigid materials try to reinforce the idea that it is only the covering which is bending, not the rigid material (just as our skin bends and stretches). Keep relating their ideas on suitable materials to the children's own movements.

Now make the puppets.

Puppet 1

This is the most straightforward design. The children should need very little help to create a satisfactory bendy person. Simply show them how the pipe-cleaners can be joined by twisting and give them the idea that the arms and legs can be linked with a simple twist.

Puppet 2

Use the A4 paper to roll tubes. Roll two pieces to make long tubes (landscape) and the other to make a shorter tube (portrait). These tubes can then be taped together with the shorter tube acting as the arms. Squash and bend the tubes to create a realistic body and joint shape. This puppet can be dressed, if desired, in the same simple style as that suggested for puppet 3 below.

Puppet 3

Form loops with the wire to create spaces which can be filled with paper held in place by adhesive tape. Each loop should be roughly proportional to the next; make a large loop for the body and a smaller loop for the head. Try to keep the loops for arms and legs in proportion too. Children will often make them much too short.

When the loops have been joined together fill each one with an appropriately-sized ball of crumpled paper and fix it in place with plenty of adhesive tape. The puppet will stand up by itself if you bend the end of the leg to form a foot. (If this does not give sufficient stability try adding a base loop, like a snow-shoe, to each foot.)

When the puppets have been completed ask the children to check if they can be moved in all the right places.

▲ What materials have you used to make your puppets?

▲ Do all the materials bend easily?

▲ Do the materials stay bent, or do they spring back into shape?

▲ What other bendy materials can you think of?

The children can make up stories which show off the bendy characteristics of their puppets. You could encourage this by reading some 'Mr Men' stories.

Suggestion(s) for extension

Some children will be able to tackle dressing the puppets. Start by asking them about suitable materials for clothing. Remind them that their puppet has to retain its flexibility so some materials would be unsuitable. This offers great opportunities for investigating textiles and flexibility.

When the children have chosen their material it can be cut out to a simple pattern (similar to that shown on page 59) and either glued or sewn into shape.

Suggestion(s) for support

Children for whom the puppet-making is too demanding can achieve the same learning objective (albeit at a lower level) by making other simple items like a Plasticine figure or a simple bracelet from pipe-cleaners. Both of these encourage the idea that some objects can be changed in shape by bending.

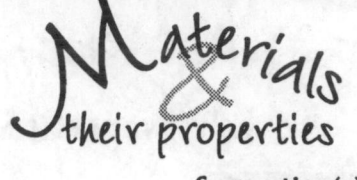

Assessment opportunities

Note those children who were unable to choose bendy materials at the beginning of the lesson. Check to see if they understand the idea better after making their puppets.

Display ideas

Group the puppets in little bendy 'families'. If the children are enthusiastic about the idea you could build some bendy furniture for them, or even create Bendy Town. Try to use as many different flexible materials as possible and label the display to reinforce the learning objective.

Other aspects of the Science PoS covered

Life Processes – 2a, 4a.
Physical Processes – 2d.

LET'S TWIST AGAIN

Some objects can be changed in shape by twisting.
✝✝ *Whole class or groups.*
🕐 *30 minutes.*

Previous skills/knowledge needed

None required.

Preparation

Make a collection of threads, string, wool and rope. These can be used to form a display a few days ahead of the lesson. Collect other items which have twisted shapes; either man-made like twisted glass, or natural, perhaps a twisted piece of tree root. You may also like to include items which contain spirals such as screws, screw-top bottles and corkscrews.

If at all possible, try to show the children how wool is spun. If you do not have the expertise yourself, your Design and Technology Inspector may be able to advise you.

Resources needed

A variety of threads, a collection of objects which show twisted shapes (these could include springs, pencil shavings,

sweet wrappers, corn dollies, twist-ties, spiral-bound books, spiral pasta shapes, and a variety of natural spiral shapes (such as shells), a bundle of pipe-cleaners, some raw wool (a spinning wheel or some other way of demonstrating wool-spinning would be a real bonus).

Language to be introduced
Thread, strand, fibre, twist, spin, spiral.

What to do
Ask the children to sort the collection of twisted items into different sets (of their choosing). Choose two objects and ask the children if they can identify three things which are the same about them and three things which are different. Ask them to describe the objects:
▲ Can you describe this shape?
▲ What does it look like/remind you of?
▲ What do you think has made it into this shape?
▲ Can you make the shape by drawing it in the air?

When the children have explored the collection of twisted shapes thoroughly, they could record their sorting activity or move on to the next part of the lesson.

Bring the children together and ask them to look at the bundle of pipe-cleaners. Hold the pipe-cleaners in your clenched fist and ask a child to pull one of the pipe-cleaners gently from your hand. When a few children have done this take the pipe-cleaners back and twist the bunch so that they are bound together like the strands of a piece of rope. Ask the children if they think it would be possible to pull the pipe-cleaners out of your hand in the same way as before. Ask them:
▲ What have we done to the pipe-cleaners?
▲ Would you like to try to pull one out of the bundle?
▲ Why is it more difficult to pull it out now?
▲ What would we have to do to pull out a single strand?
Now give out pieces of string, wool, yarn and other items from the collection of threads. Ask the children:
▲ Can you see anything about your piece of string/wool that is the same as the pipe-cleaners?
▲ Is it easy to unravel your thread?
▲ How many strands do you think have been put together to make your piece of thread?
▲ Can you take them apart?
If you have been able to resource a spinning activity this is where it would come in. In any case it is worth making the connection here between the making of fibres and the act of spinning or, as it says in the learning objective, twisting.

Suggestion(s) for extension
If the children have understood that objects can be changed in shape by twisting then challenge them to think of other materials which could be changed by twisting. Continuing the theme of fibres could lead children to investigate knots, plaits, weaving, finger-knitting, growth of plants, architectural features, cooking, and so on. This should help them to recognise the difference between materials which have been twisted and those which have been moulded, curved, woven or planted to give the appearance of being twisted.

Suggestion(s) for support

For younger and less able children some reinforcement of the idea of twisting could be provided through play with malleable materials such as salt dough (see recipe on page 157) and clay.

Assessment opportunities

Opportunities for assessment come mainly in the discussion or question and answer sessions. Try to assess whether or not the children can generalise from the particular item they are handling to the more 'difficult concept that many things can be changed in shape by twisting. You could ask a series of questions to elicit more information:

▲ Could you twist wood to make it change its shape?
▲ Could you twist metal to make it change its shape?
▲ Could you twist glass to make it change its shape?
▲ Could you twist paper to make it change its shape?

Exercise caution here as many things can be twisted (such as glass, when it is molten). Check where children's ideas are coming from by asking:

▲ Where have you seen that?

Display ideas

Make a display of the twisted items in your collection and display the children's recording nearby. Give the display a caption to reinforce the learning objective, such as 'Have all these items been twisted?'

Other aspects of the Science PoS covered

Experimental and Investigative Science – various aspects of this will be covered, depending on the individual teacher's approach.

STRETCHY FABRIC

Some objects can be changed in shape by stretching.
†† *Whole class or group.*
🕒 *40 minutes.*

Previous skills/knowledge needed

No special skills are required for the first part of the lesson but teachers will need to consider the suitability of the puppet-making activity for children in their group and modify it if necessary.

Preparation

Make a collection of textiles including stretchy and not-so-stretchy fabrics. Ask the children to bring in one old sock each which could be used for a puppet. (It is usually better to use adult socks for this.) Buy one new pair of socks and keep the label on to show the children.

Resources needed

A collection of textiles, one sock per child, a small amount of card (to make the features of the puppet), sticky fixers (or some other way of sticking the features to the socks), a brand new pair of socks with the label still on.

You may also wish to provide the children with a pair of eyes each. These are available from textile shops and school suppliers.

Language to be introduced

Stretch, stretchy, stretched, stretchiness, stretchiest, flexible, bend.

What to do

Sort the collection of materials. Allow the children to set their own criteria to begin with, then impose the idea of 'stretchiness' if it has not already been introduced. Once the collection has been sorted according to stretchiness take one example from each category and compare them:

▲ How far do you think we can make this one stretch?
▲ How does it compare with this one?
▲ Which do you think would be the stretchiest fabric?
▲ How far can we stretch this one?

The children can measure or compare the different pieces of fabric.

Discuss with the children the reasons for fabrics being stretchy. If pupils have already completed the lesson on bending ('The bendy puppet' on page 59) you can relate the need for stretchiness to our ability to bend at the joints. If the children have not covered the work in this lesson you may wish to discuss the way in which human beings move, and the need for flexible fabrics.

Show the children the new pair of socks and explain the way in which sock size is related to shoe size. Socks stretch to fit a wide range of foot sizes but shoes do not stretch and

are made to fit one size only. Children could now be given an opportunity to take off their shoes and look at their own socks. Ask them first to see how much they can wiggle their toes inside their shoes. Then suggest they take their shoes off and try wiggling their toes again.

Ask the children to examine the socks they have brought in. Point out that the stretchiness of the sock makes it ideal for puppet-making. Show that by putting your hand in the end of the sock you can make a kind of mouth movement. Finish the lesson by helping the children make their puppets by adding simple features to the end of the socks.

Suggestion(s) for extension
This lesson provides opportunities to investigate stretchiness. Further ideas on this are explored in detail in the chapter on Investigations (see page 99).

Suggestion(s) for support
The measuring activity can be recorded by stretching the fabrics over a large piece of paper and putting a mark to show the extent of the stretching.

Assessment opportunities
Watch the children as they sort the materials for stretchiness. There is no clear division between what is and what is not stretchy so take note of those who find their own ways of deciding which set a particular sample should be put in. They may set their own criterion for stretchiness:
'I've put all the ones which are stretchier than this into the first set and all the others into the second set.'

Some children may also suggest creating a third set for samples about which they are not sure, while others may propose carrying out a test to assess stretchiness. All of these ideas show a higher level of operation in science and should be noted.

Display ideas
Display the collection of materials with suitable questions such as: 'Which material is the stretchiest?'

Mount some of the children's puppets behind the display with the caption: 'We made these puppets out of stretchy material.'

Other aspects of the Science PoS covered
Experimental and Investigative Science – various aspects of this will be covered, depending on the individual teacher's approach.

ICEBERGS

To describe the way in which water changes when it is cooled.
✝✝ *Small groups.*
🕐 *35 minutes.*

Previous skills/knowledge needed
Children should be aware of the concepts of hot and cold as they relate to themselves. This can be achieved by taking the children outside on a cold day or by comparing summer and winter clothing. For further ideas see the lesson called 'Materials with special uses' on page 55.

Preparation
Fill one or more balloons with water and place them in a freezer overnight. Also freeze some ice-cubes in ice cube bags. If you are going to use your home freezer for this you will need to prepare some means of transporting the ice to school and arrange to store it there. A cool box filled with a good insulator such as polystyrene chips or paper should be adequate. In the classroom you will need to part-fill your water containers and set them where pupils can gather around them.

Resources needed
A water tray, preferably one with transparent sides (if you want to run this activity with more than one group at a time, plastic aquaria are suitable), a few items which will show the

Materials & their properties

▲ Would the ice be soaked up by the sponge?
▲ How is the ice like the water?
▲ How is it different?

Children find the ball of ice fascinating, and may want to draw what they see.

The ice ball will soon begin to melt, so place it in the plastic container. Ask the children what they think is happening to the ice:

▲ How would you stop it from melting?
▲ Could we put it somewhere in the room to make it melt more slowly?
▲ Where would be a bad place to put it?

At this point you could weigh the ice ball, then see if it loses weight as it grows smaller. This could turn into a complicated investigation, depending on the ability levels of the children. Some children might suggest weighing the melt water with the diminishing ice ball!

To complete this part of the lesson, ask the children what they think will happen if the ice ball is put in the water tray. Accept all opinions, then test their ideas by trying this out.

Now ask the children to summarise what they have learned about what happens to water when it is frozen:

▲ What can water do that ice cannot?
▲ What other differences can they identify between ice and water?

This would make a good recording activity for more able children.

Suggestion(s) for extension

Ask the children how they could use the ice to find out about different temperatures in different parts of the room.

▲ Where do you think it will be coldest?
▲ Where will the ice melt quickest?
▲ How can we tell if one place is hotter than another?

Suggestion(s) for support

Some children would benefit from linguistic support when recording the behaviour of the water and ice. Words suggested in 'Language to be introduced' (above) could be used to create a language support sheet. Alternatively, spend time during the lesson drawing the language from the children, then add this to a vocabulary list on the board.

Assessment opportunities

Check to see if the children have made the connection between water and ice. Ask them to explain how ice is formed outdoors or in a freezer. Do they realise that water must be present before ice can form? Explore their understanding by asking them about rain, snow and hail.

Other aspects of the Science PoS covered

Experimental and Investigative Science – various aspects of this will be covered, depending on the individual teacher's approach.

way in which water behaves (such as a jug for pouring, a sponge for absorption, a plastic bottle to show how water pushes the air out when the bottle is submerged), ice balloons, a large plastic container (perhaps a drawer tray), scissors, weighing scales, a pair of gloves.

Language to be introduced

Pour, soak up, splash, float, bubbles, melt, cold, warm, see-through, transparent, cloudy, opaque, cracked, freeze, frozen, hard, slippery.

What to do

Gather your group of children around the water tray. Talk to them about the way in which water behaves. Ask them:

▲ How do you know this is water?
▲ What does water look like?
▲ What does water do when you push a bottle under it?
▲ What will water do when we put this dry sponge into it?

Repeat this last question for a number of objects.

Now take out an ice balloon. Ask the children to tell you what they think is inside the balloon. Would they be surprised if you told them there was water in the balloon?

Cut the balloon open with the scissors and ask them to look closely at what is inside. Check to make sure they know that it is a ball of ice. Ask them:

▲ How do you think I made this?
▲ What do you see when you look closely at the ice?

MELTING CHOCOLATE

To describe the way in which some materials change when they are heated or cooled.

†† *Small groups.*

⏱ *40 minutes.*

⚠ *Observe school cookery safety and hygiene guidelines during this lesson. Provide adequate adult supervision.*

Previous skills/knowledge needed

Children should have already considered the effect of heating on chocolate and other substances. This can easily be drawn from their own experience of holding chocolate bars or eating ice-cream.

Preparation

Organise your extra helpers and buy the ingredients for the cookery activity. Photocopy the recipe on page 139.

Resources needed

Pyrex-type transparent pudding basin, plastic spoons, cooking ingredients (see the photocopiable sheet on page 139 for recipe).

You will also need a means of melting chocolate – ideally a microwave oven as this allows a small group of children the opportunity to watch the chocolate melt. If you do not have access to a microwave you will have to melt the chocolate in a bowl over a saucepan of hot water, but in this case do not allow children to get too close. The cakes can be cooked in a microwave or a conventional oven.

Language to be introduced

Change, melt, runny, hard, solid, heat, warm, hot, rise, mixture, heating, cooling, warmth, heat.

What to do

Start the lesson as a discussion with all the children who are going to cook (the whole class, if appropriate). Ask them to think about the effect heat has on things:

▲ What happens to snow or ice when the sun shines on them?

▲ What happens to ice-creams and lollies on a hot day?

▲ What happens to the chocolate on a biscuit when a baby holds it with warm hands?

Tell the children that they are going to melt some ingredients in order to make cakes. They will make butter or margarine melt and also chocolate.

Take the cooking group to the microwave and, having placed the chocolate and butter or margarine in the bowl melt the ingredients on full power (if you have two bowls melt the ingredients separately and then mix). Ask the children to describe what they see happening as they look through the microwave door.

When the ingredients have melted ask the children to describe the changes which have taken place:

▲ What are the differences between the melted chocolate and the chocolate in the bar?

▲ How has the butter or margarine changed?

Now use your ingredients to make the cake (see page 139), asking the children to note the changes which are taking place as the cake is cooking:

▲ What is happening to the cake mixture?

▲ What do you think is making the cake mixture change?

Suggestion(s) for extension

Older and more able children may be able to make a list of things which change as a result of heating and cooling. This will depend on their experience but could include the effects of heat on: clay, dough, eggs, wet things (such as clothes or hair), puddles, water in a kettle.

Discuss the effects of fire or extreme heat, reinforcing safety issues. To complement the effects of heating you could also explore the effects of cooling by asking the children to think about freezers and their uses.

Suggestion(s) for support
Younger and less able children may need support at the beginning of the lesson. Make sure they understand the idea of melting (the lesson called 'Icebergs', on page 63 may be helpful for this).

Assessment opportunities
Make a note of pupils who can/cannot make the connection between the melted chocolate and the original solid block. Ask the children:
▲ Is this still chocolate?
▲ What has changed?
This can be repeated for any ingredients which change during the course of the lesson.

Opportunities for IT
Pupils could use a concept keyboard linked to a word processor to sequence the various parts of the cooking activity. The overlay could contain pictures, or sentences, appropriate to the age and ability of the children. Alternatively, children could write the instructions or describe what happened using a word processor. They could work in pairs or groups, or with an adult to scribe their explanation of how they made the chocolate cake.

Display ideas
Create a display with pictures or photos of the children cooking, and the finished cake!

Other aspects of the Science PoS covered
Experimental and Investigative Science – various aspects of this will be covered depending on the individual teacher's approach.

Reference to photocopiable sheet
The photocopiable sheet on page 139 provides the recipe and method for the chocolate cake. The cake can be cooked in the microwave or conventional oven.

The children can use it as a reading sheet or as support for any written accounts they may do of the activity.

Chewy chocolate cake recipe

75g broken plain chocolate
100g butter
2 eggs
225g sugar
1 teaspoon of vanilla essence
100g plain flour

Line a 20cm square box with plastic cling film.
Put chocolate and butter in a see-through bowl and microwave on high for 1½–2 minutes.
Put the eggs, sugar and vanilla essence into another bowl and beat together until thick and creamy.

Mix in the flour, and the chocolate mixture, adding one tablespoon of each at a time.
Spoon the mixture into the square box and smooth the top.
Microwave on high for 5 or 6 minutes, turning the dish every minute if the microwave does not have a turntable.
(The cake can also be cooked in a conventional oven at 180°C, Gas Mark 5 for 30–40 minutes.)

Physical processes

This section of the book contains activities on electricity, forces and motion and light and sound. These areas of study are potentially hazardous, so teachers should carry out a risk assessment before proceeding with any practical science lesson. Health and safety teaching should also be included as part of each lesson where it is appropriate.

The activities in this section provide experiences which will improve children's knowledge of materials and also provide opportunities for them to develop their practical scientific skills. Throughout these activities the emphasis is on first-hand experience, which young children need if they are to build their conceptual frameworks and hence their knowledge and understanding of the world.

The resources required for the lessons in this section include:
▲ batteries, bulbs and related electrical equipment;
▲ water and sand trays;
▲ Plasticine, clay and salt-water dough;
▲ musical instruments, especially tuning forks and percussion instruments.

In the lesson 'Light and reflection' (page 79), a collection of shiny objects is required. This is a useful resource for many areas of science so should be stored with your science resources for subsequent use.

ELECTRICITY AND SAFETY

Mains electricity is dangerous and can kill you.

†† *Class discussion followed by individual worksheets.*

⏱ *35 minutes.*

Previous skills/knowledge needed

Teachers will need to decide if the suggested worksheet is appropriate. It will probably already be part of the school's safety policy that no child is permitted to plug in electrical appliances. This could be a starting point for discussion. Sensitivity will be required if any children have direct experience of household accidents.

Preparation

Collect a number of common, portable, household electrical appliances. Try to include items which present different sorts of dangers, perhaps a kettle (which could burn you) or a drill (which could pierce your skin). Also include items which are powered by mains electricity but are safe to play with under adult supervision, such as a computer or a train set. You may also like to include some battery-powered toys at this stage.

Resources needed

A collection of common household appliances, sorting rings, copies of the photocopiable sheets on pages 140 and 141.

Language to be introduced

Electricity, mains, electrical appliances, plug, lead, cable, wires, switch, safe, dangerous.

What to do

Talk to the children about school rules which govern the use of electrical appliances. Do they have rules at home? Why is it a good idea to have rules? Ask the children:

▲ Which of these things are you allowed to touch?

▲ Which must you never touch?

▲ Which, if any, are completely safe?

▲ Which parts are dangerous?

Help the children to sort the collection of electrical appliances. If you have included battery-powered toys the sorting exercise can involve three sets:

▲ Set 1 – never touch;

▲ Set 2 – never touch the plug;

▲ Set 3 – safe to play with.

Use copies of the photocopiable sheet on page 140 or large sheets of paper to allow the children to represent potentially dangerous electrical items.

Suggestion(s) for extension

Add other items to the collection and see if the children can put them in the right set. Ask the children to place warning triangles near any source of electrical danger (use the photocopiable sheet on page 141).

Explain why it is dangerous to switch things on with wet hands and why we don't have sockets and ordinary switches in bathrooms.

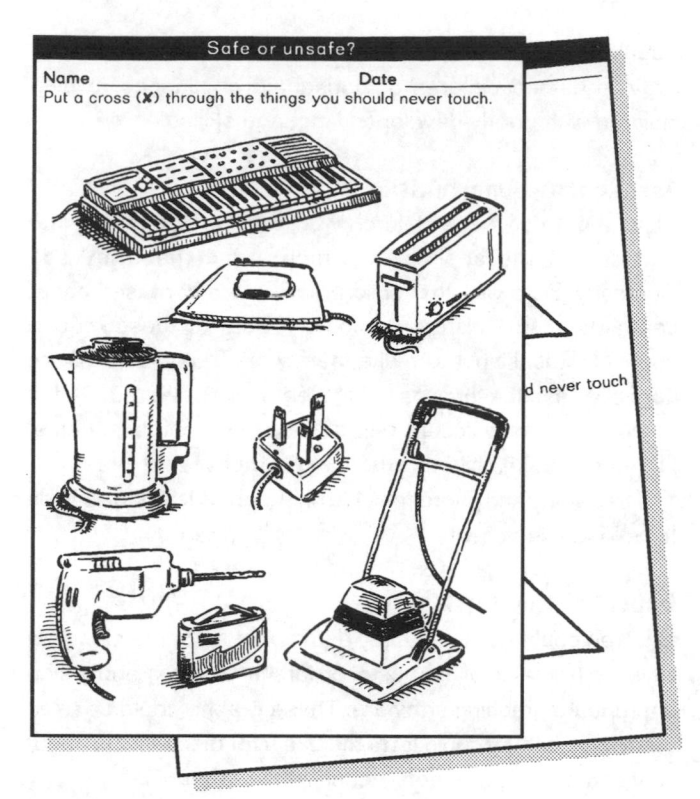

Safe or unsafe?

Name _____ Date _____
Put a cross (✗) through the things you should never touch.

d never touch

USING ELECTRICITY

Many everyday appliances use electricity.
✦✦ *This lesson could be taught to the whole class or to groups in turn.*
🕐 *40 minutes.*
⚠ *Children should be taught about the potential danger of electrical supplies and appliances. 'Electricity and safety', the lesson on page 68, would be useful for teaching ideas on electrical safety.*

Previous skills/knowledge needed

The children's previous experience will dictate the degree to which they can organise their own collection of information for the survey (see the photocopiable sheet on page 142).

Preparation

Make a collection of everyday portable appliances. You could include mains-powered radios, hairdryers, drills, can-openers, heaters, alarm clocks, keyboards, lamps, kettles, toasters, sandwich-makers, electric blankets. As a separate collection you may like to have a few items which are specifically related to school, such as a slide projector, OHP or electric pencil sharpener. Take copies of the sheet on page 142.

Resources needed

A collection of portable electric appliances, copies of the photocopiable sheet on page 142.

Suggestion(s) for support

Magazines and colour supplements will provide a good picture resource for those children who may find illustrative material helpful when recording the sorting activity or identifying appliances which they are not allowed to touch.

Assessment opportunities

The recording activities within the lesson should provide opportunities for teacher/pupil discussion where necessary.

Display ideas

Display the appliances and toys sorted into their different groups with the warning triangles and plug covers. To add emphasis you could place the 'never touch' group at a level where they are out of the children's reach.

Contact your local health and safety officer or your local electricity board for further information, advice and resources.

Other aspects of the Science PoS covered

None.

Reference to photocopiable sheets

In the sheet on page 140 children are asked to cross out the things they should never touch. It may be appropriate to use thick black felt-tipped pens to emphasise the dangerous nature of the appliances.

The sheet on page 141 contains two 'danger' signs which can be coloured bright red, cut out and displayed around the classroom and school next to items of equipment and appliances that the children should never touch. This will reinforce the learning objective that electricity is dangerous.

Language to be introduced

Plugs, cables, switches, portable appliances, plus the names of the electrical appliances in your collection.

What to do

Talk to the children and help them identify what is common to all or most of the appliances, in other words help them to recognise those features which show the appliances are electrical – the fact that they have plugs, cables, switches. Ask the children:
▲ What makes all these things work?
▲ How can you tell that this uses electricity?
▲ Do all these things have switches/cables/plugs?

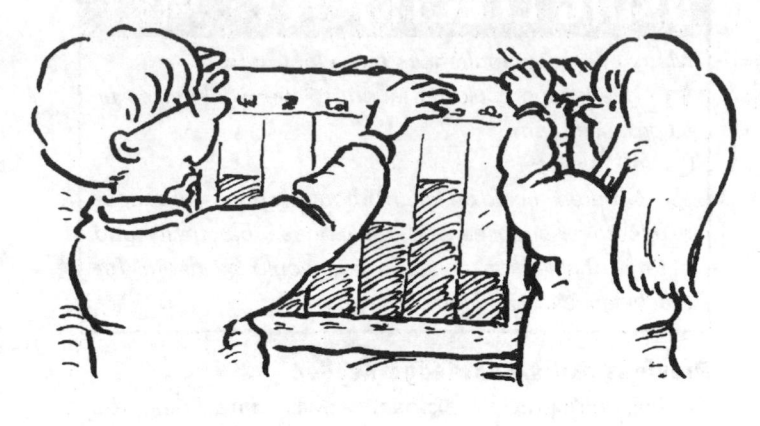

Help the children to identify other things in the classroom which use electricity. Do these also have plugs, cables and switches? Is there anything in the classroom which you would not usually find in a home?

Sort the collection. The children may have their own suggestions for grouping the items. If they do not you could choose from the following sorting criteria:
▲ home/school
▲ bedroom/kitchen/sitting-room/garage, and so on.

At this point you could photograph the sorting activity or draw and label the appliances in their groups. The photocopiable sheet on page 142 could be useful for this.

The lesson can be stopped at this point, and the sorting exercise recorded. More able children could be encouraged to make a survey of household appliances by asking them about what they have at home. Sensitivity may have to be exercised in the collection of this information so that neither children nor parents are offended or upset.

Suggestion(s) for extension

Introduce additional items to the collection and ask the children to sort them into the appropriate groups.

If you think the children are ready to make the conceptual leap, you could introduce some battery-powered items and discuss the similarities and differences between these and mains-powered appliances.

Individual children could turn the raw data from the survey of home appliances into tables and charts. Some children may also be able to make a survey of favourite electrical toys within the class.

Suggestion(s) for support
Provide named pictures of household appliances to help children with poorly-developed language skills.

Assessment opportunities
Make a note of those children who can/cannot identify the features of the appliances which show that they use electricity. Be aware that children are often confused about central heating radiators and cars – both of these require some electrical input to make them work, but we would not normally describe them as being electrically powered. At this stage it is best to accept pupils' views on confusing items! Note only those children who make significant errors.

The survey and photocopiable sheet provide opportunities for skills assessment.

Opportunities for IT
Children could use the survey data about favourite electrical toys or home appliances to create a block graph using appropriate graphing software. These graphs could be used for display or they could form the basis for discussions about why some items are more popular than others.

Display ideas
Create a display using your collection of electrical appliances. These can be sorted into their groups and labelled. You could add some open-ended questions such as:
▲ Where would we normally find these?
▲ What makes these things work?
▲ Do you know which ones work by battery?

The display could also include the raw data from the survey of household appliances and any charts or graphs which have been generated from this data.

Other aspects of the Science PoS covered
The photocopiable sheet on page 142 offers opportunities for the children to practise a skill essential to scientific investigations.

Reference to photocopiable sheet
Page 142 provides a survey sheet which the children can complete at school or at home. The left-hand column has been left blank for you to enter your own survey areas, such as rooms in a house, areas in the school, and so on. The children should place a tick in the corresponding row for each electrical appliance found there.

MAKING SIMPLE CIRCUITS

To learn how to make things work by constructing a simple circuit.

✝✝ *Individual activity within small groups. The number of individuals able to work on this activity at one time will be dictated by the amount of equipment available.*

🕐 *30 minutes.*

⚠ *Children should be taught about the potential danger of mains electricity. Care should be taken that the children do not short the batteries while investigating them. For this reason rechargeable batteries are **not** suitable for use in this lesson.*

Previous skills/knowledge needed

It would be helpful if the children could see and possibly handle some of the electrical equipment before starting the activity. If they have not used the equipment before they will need time to look at the different objects and learn the names of individual items.

Preparation

Check the components to ensure they are in working order. Check that the voltage of your batteries, bulbs and other components are compatible.

Most schools use 6 volt buzzers. These will work quite well with 4.5 volt batteries (such as EverReady 1289), 3.5 volt bulbs would be compatible with these batteries.

Be careful to wire buzzers the right way round. Join the red wire to the positive terminal and the black to the negative.

Set out the resources for your group or groups where they will be accessible but not available for 'free play'. Duplicate the photocopiable sheet on page 143 if required.

Resources needed

You will need sufficient batteries, wires, bulbs, bulb holders and buzzers for individual children to be able to make a circuit. A range of different types of wire is useful, some with crocodile clips, some without; some with plastic insulation, some without. Wire-strippers or some other means of removing the plastic insulation on the wire will also be needed.

Language to be introduced

Battery, bulb, bulb holder, wire, wire-strippers, buzzer, crocodile clips, crocodile lead, circuit.

What to do

Give the children all the equipment with the exception of the buzzers. Keep the buzzers until later to protect your own sanity! Let the children investigate the materials but warn them not to smash the bulbs and watch them to make sure they don't short the batteries (if they join both ends or put a wire across the terminals, the batteries will very quickly lose their charge).

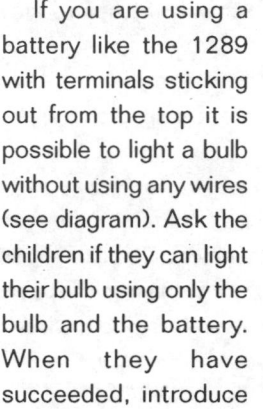

If you are using a battery like the 1289 with terminals sticking out from the top it is possible to light a bulb without using any wires (see diagram). Ask the children if they can light their bulb using only the bulb and the battery. When they have succeeded, introduce the bulb holders and try again. You can explain that bulb holders are used because it is more convenient than holding the bulbs ourselves. When the pupils have made the bulbs work in the holders you can introduce the wire.

It usually helps to start off with wire that has no insulation on it at all. Children who are presented with insulated wire often don't realise that the wire is continuous inside the plastic coating. This then acts as a barrier to their understanding of an electrical circuit. Ask the children:

▲ What is making your bulb work?

▲ Can you switch it on and off?

Next introduce the coated insulated wire, and ask:

▲ Why do you think we scrape the plastic covering off the ends of the wire?

▲ Why do you think we use crocodile clips/bulb holders?

The buzzers can be introduced at this stage. Do the children know what would happen if they left their bulb or buzzer on for too long? Do they understand that the power will be used up?

Once they have had the opportunity to construct a number of simple circuits you can tell the children that the electricity flows from the battery, through the bulb or buzzer and back to the battery again. Use of an analogy for the flow of electricity can sometimes help children gain a deeper understanding. You may wish to explain that the electricity flows through the wires like water flows through pipes, or that the electrical circuit is a bit like a running track in a stadium where athletes are running round as fast as they can, gradually using up their energy.

SCIENCE

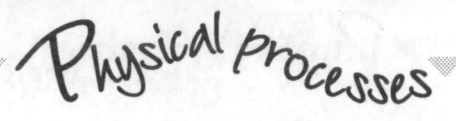
Ask the children to cut out the pictures and words from the photocopiable sheet on page 143 and use them to create labelled diagrams of their circuits.

Suggestion(s) for extension
Ask the children to try to light more than one bulb in their circuits.

Older and more able children could be presented with a range of conductors and non-conductors and asked to place them in their circuits. Try including a pencil as a conductor and make a collection of everyday classroom items to go with it. Ask the children to predict which materials will let the electricity flow through them and which will not *before* they actually try them out.

You could also investigate how long it takes a (rechargeable) battery to run down in a toy or torch.

Suggestion(s) for support
Younger and less able children may be confused if they are presented with too much material at once. Stick to single components and small quantities of wire with your least able groups until you are sure that they have understood the basic learning objective.

Assessment opportunities
It is difficult to judge to what extent some children are copying others in this activity. If you wish to assess the children it is probably best to do the activity individually. This could be done on a separate occasion, or include the introduction of a different component, such as a motor. Use the photocopiable sheet on page 143.

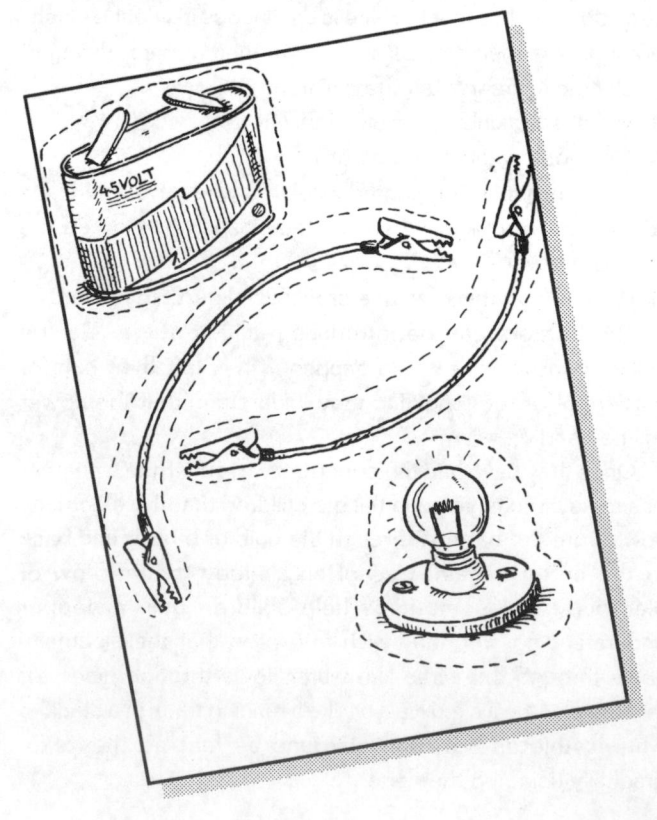

Alternatively, check if pupils have grasped the idea of a simple circuit by asking them to add extra pieces of wire to the circuit, then watching to see where they put them.

Display ideas
Make an interactive display using batteries, bulbs and wires. Write some questions on card to accompany the display (perhaps those suggested in the 'What to do' section above). Display an example of a completed circuit alongside other battery-powered items such as toys, clocks and torches.

Other aspects of the Science PoS covered
Experimental and Investigative Science – aspects of this are covered in the extension activity.

Reference to photocopiable sheet
The children should cut around the dotted lines on the photocopiable sheet on page 143, then re-assemble the pieces to make a picture of a complete circuit. Teachers will need to provide appropriate support so that children are given maximum opportunity to show if they understand the principle of making a circuit.

SWITCHING ON AND OFF

A complete circuit is needed to make electrical things work.

†† *Individual activity within small groups. The number of individuals able to work on this activity at one time will be dictated by the quantity of equipment available.*

🕐 *30 minutes.*

⚠ *Children should be taught about the potential danger of mains electricity. Batteries should be handled correctly and care must be taken that they are not shorted, or damaged. Rechargeable batteries are **not** suitable for this activity.*

Preparation
The components should be checked to ensure they are in working order and compatible.

Resources needed
You will need sufficient batteries, bulbs, bulb holders, buzzers and wire for individual children to make a circuit. You will also need material with which to make simple switches. A small quantity of kitchen foil per pupil will suffice, but it may also be helpful to have access to the following: sticky tape, paper-clips, drawing pins, paper-fasteners, small sections of pinboard.

Language to be introduced
Switch, switching on, switching off, circuit, broken circuit, complete circuit.

SCIENCE

What to do

Give the children enough material to construct a simple circuit and make a bulb light. Encourage them to see if they can make the bulb switch on and off. Can they break the circuit in different places to switch the light on and off? Ask the children:

▲ When does the bulb switch off?

▲ What do we need to make a bulb work?

▲ What happens if the circuit is broken?

As a teacher demonstration, introduce a piece of foil to the circuit. Try the piece of foil in different places in the circuit to show that it does not matter where the foil is placed, as long as the circuit is still complete. While the bulb is alight break the circuit by literally ripping the piece of foil in two. Ask the children to explain what has happened, then encourage them to do the same with their circuits, making sure that they do not short the batteries by placing the foil across the terminals. Challenge them to try to make their bulbs light with a gap in the circuit. Ask them:

▲ Can we put the foil anywhere in the circuit?

▲ What is happening when we break the foil?

▲ Can you use your piece of foil to switch the bulb on and off?

If necessary, show them how to make the bulb flash on and off by bending the foil up and down. This is a switch. See if the children can make the conceptual leap that this switch is like the switches on electrical appliances in the room.

To make the foil switches more durable, and easier to handle, they can be stiffened with card and pinned or taped to a small piece of board.

If you feel that the children have understood the idea of the switches then you can substitute paper-clips or paper-fasteners for the foil. Similarly, buzzers can be substituted for the bulbs.

Suggestion(s) for extension

Make different switches and try them in the circuits.

Replace your home-made switch with a commercially produced one. Try lighting two bulbs from one battery and switching them on and off.

The construction of a model with a switching mechanism would form a natural extension of this work.

Suggestion(s) for support

If children are unable to grasp the idea of switches it is best to allow them to spend more time creating simple electrical circuits.

Assessment opportunities

Careful observation of the children carrying out the activities outlined above should provide a good indication of their understanding. If you are unsure whether or not certain individuals have grasped the learning objective you could ask them to repeat some of the lesson on their own, possibly using a different series of components.

A good assessment activity for the whole of this section on electricity would be to ask the children to apply what they have learned by designing and making a model, perhaps a house or a car with lights which switch on and off.

Opportunities for IT

Children can be introduced to the simple elements of control in this work, realising that switches can be used to control electrical devices. They might then discuss other places and devices which are controlled – these could range from simple switches to turn on lights or a toy, to complex control mechanisms such as those in washing machines and video recorders.

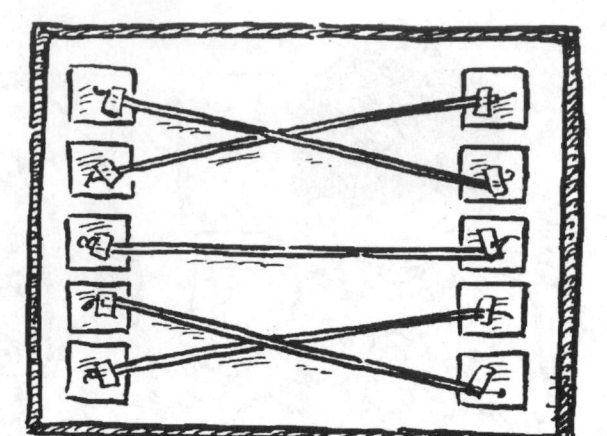

Display ideas

Make an interactive display using simple circuits and switches, possibly a series of lights which come on only when the right wires are joined. This can be used to reinforce simple number bonds or, with younger children, colours or shapes (see above).

Other aspects of the Science PoS covered

Experimental and Investigative Science – various aspects of this will be covered, depending on the individual teacher's approach.

THE EVERYDAY LANGUAGE OF FORCES AND MOTION

To be able to describe the movement of familiar things.
†† *Whole-class lesson in a hall or outside.*
🕐 *35 minutes.*
⚠ *Your usual PE safety guidelines should be applied.*

Previous skills/knowledge needed

None required.

Preparation

If you do not have sufficient playground or hall markings you will need to draw your own chalk lines. Draw patterns and shapes on the hall floor or in the playground which will help the children experience the feeling of movement and forces as they run along them. These can include letter shapes, road-markings, zigzags and spirals. Leave room to add the children's own suggestions during the course of the lesson.

Resources needed

Several pieces of playground chalk. (If you want to make a more permanent record of the patterns created by the children you will also need large sheets of paper and crayons or you could use a still or video camera).

Language to be introduced

Faster, slower, quickly, slowly, speed up, slow down, turn right, turn left, swerve, forwards, backwards, sideways, change direction, zigzag, spiral, shape, spin, wavy, forces, speed, pushes, pulls.

What to do

In your PE lesson involve pupils in activities which introduce them to the language of movement. Let them follow the lines marked on the floor and talk about the different shapes and movements. Ask the children:
▲ Can you go forwards/backwards/sideways?
▲ Can you change your speed?

Show the children how to run along pathways outlining invisible shapes such as circles or squares. Work on pathways of letter and number shapes, possibly asking them to make the shape of the first letter of their name.

Repeat the activity to include moving quickly and slowly, forwards, backwards and sideways. Ask pupils to describe their movements.

Encourage the children to rush around, being careful to avoid each other as they do so. Introduce the idea of swerving, stopping and starting. The children can pretend to be cars, or on their bikes, and do sudden stops and fast starts. Ask the children:
▲ Can you feel the pushes as you start, stop or change direction?
▲ Where can you feel them?
▲ Which part of you feels the forces?

When you have practised a range of movements, allow the children to create their own patterns, asking questions such as:
▲ Can you make a pattern with a zigzag?
▲ Can you find a wavy letter?
▲ What different shapes can you make?

At this point you may wish to record some of the shapes being made. You could use a camera or ask the children to draw their patterns on large sheets of paper.

Suggestion(s) for extension
Add mats and simple apparatus to increase the range of movements being investigated. Try rolls and twists, asking the children where they feel the forces acting as they carry out these movements. Introduce a road safety element into this lesson, encouraging children to think about bicycle helmets and injuries.

Suggestion(s) for support
Younger and less able children will need time to develop their experiences of movement. Use this lesson as one short element in a series of PE lessons.

Assessment opportunities
Watch the children as you issue instructions such as 'speed up' or 'swerve in and out' to see who understands the language.

Opportunities for IT
Children could use a floor turtle, linked to the computer, or a Roamer controllable vehicle to experiment with some of the language of movement such as 'backwards', 'forwards', 'turn', 'right' and 'left'. They could attempt to make the Roamer move around a simple course, or get it to draw a square or other shape on large sheets of paper. Children may also begin to understand the need for accurate commands if Roamer is to move exactly where they want it to go.

Display ideas
Ask the children to draw their floor patterns on large sheets of paper and to explain the movements in words, and by using arrows to show directions. Cartoons are a good means of showing movement in visual form. Consider watching 'Tom and Jerry' on video, then using some of the language with which the children describe the movements of the cartoon characters to enhance your display.

Other aspects of the Science PoS covered
Life Processes and Living Things – 1b.

PUSHES AND PULLS

Pushes and pulls make things move.
†† *Small-group practical followed by individual worksheets.*
🕐 *35 minutes.*
⚠ *Children should not be allowed to lift, push or pull excessively heavy loads. The activities suggested in this lesson must be closely supervised.*

Previous skills/knowledge needed
It would be helpful if children had used the language of pushes and pulls as part of their PE curriculum (see 'The everyday language of forces and motion' on page 74).

Preparation
Bring a heavy object into the room, one which the children would find difficult to move (a bag of clay or sand would be ideal). Place it in the opposite corner of the room from the sand tray, craft area or wherever it would normally be used. Take one copy of the photocopiable sheet on page 144 for each member of your group.

Resources needed
In addition to the heavy bag of clay or sand you could, if possible, provide a simple trolley (a toddler truck would do) and a range of different materials which might help the children investigate pushes and pulls. These could include: some sheets of plastic, large sheets of paper or card, thin rope, pieces of carpet, sacking or netting. Access to a sand or water tray, a ball.

Language to be introduced
Push, pull, lift, roll, tug, heavy, heave, strain.

What to do
Explain to the children that they are being set a challenge which they must solve. The sand (or clay) has been left in the wrong place and it is too heavy to lift.
▲ Why shouldn't we lift heavy things?
▲ How can we get it across the room?
  Discuss the different options with the children:
▲ Does anyone think it would be easier to push, pull or roll the bag?

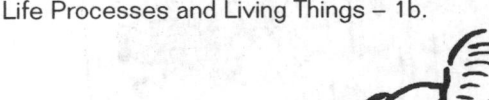

Get them to try out each in turn, but be aware that the answer to the question is not important and will vary according to the object being moved, the texture of the ground surface and the position of the children relative to the object. The question is a starting point to extend thinking and help understanding.

▲ Is rolling like pushing or like pulling?

▲ Would it make a difference if we put the bag on this sheet of plastic or card?

▲ Would this piece of rope make a difference? What? How?

▲ Would the bag be easier to move if we used this trolley? Why?

The children can record their activities by drawing themselves pushing, pulling or rolling the heavy object. Older and more able children could add arrows to show the direction of the force being exerted (see below). The photocopiable sheet on page 144 gives opportunities for the ideas developed in this lesson to be applied in different contexts.

Suggestion(s) for extension

Some children may be able to rank the forces in order of effectiveness, for example 'it is easier to push/roll/pull the heavy bag'. Similarly they may be able to compare how easy it is to pull the bag over different surfaces such as a carpet compared with a tiled floor.

Ask the children to think about other situations in which pushes and pulls make things move. Use examples in the sand and water tray to extend thinking. Talk about the objects which are floating in the water tray.

▲ Can the children feel the push of the object?

▲ What is pushing the object up?

This example is made more spectacular if a balloon or ball is used. Similarly, the movement of sand wheels in the sand tray uses the push of the sand to create movement.

Suggestion(s) for support

Younger and less able children will need to work on a limited range of variables. You may wish to introduce the heavy object by itself to begin with (without ropes, trolleys and other items) so that the children are able to focus on the forces which can be exerted with their own bodies.

Assessment opportunities

Note those children who use the language of forces correctly. Hand out copies of the photocopiable sheet on page 144 and ask the children to use arrows to show the direction of the pushes and pulls, writing answers according to their ability.

Opportunities for IT

Younger children could record their understanding of this work using a concept keyboard linked to a word processor. The overlay could include pictures of different objects and words such as 'push', 'pull' and link words such as 'you', 'I' and so on. Children could then link the words to the pictures in simple sentences, such as 'You push a weighing scale'.

Display ideas

Take photographs of the children at work to form a display on pushes and pulls. The display could include a range of common items which use pushes and pulls to make them work such as weighing scales, pumps, doorbells or handles.

Other aspects of the Science PoS covered

Experimental and Investigative Science – various aspects of this will be covered depending on the individual teacher's approach.

Reference to photocopiable sheet

The photocopiable sheet on page 144 will show pupils' understanding of the activity. It requires the children to fill in the missing words 'push' or 'pull' to finish the sentences.

It may be necessary to read each sentence to the less able children, encouraging them to answer before showing them which word they need to insert.

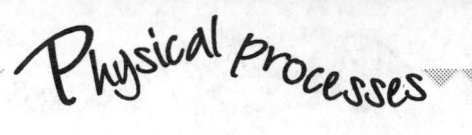

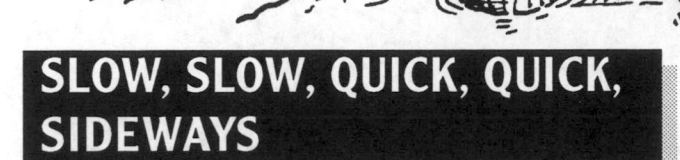

SLOW, SLOW, QUICK, QUICK, SIDEWAYS

Forces can make things speed up, slow down or change direction.

†† *Small-group practical.*

🕐 *45 minutes.*

⚠ *Mains-powered fans should not be used with this activity.*

Previous skills/knowledge needed

It would be helpful if children had used the language of forces in different contexts (see lessons on pages 74 and 75 of this chapter for ideas).

Preparation

Part-fill your water containers and set them ready for action.

Resources needed

The children will need access to a number of water trays or containers – one between two is ideal. Containers can include your water tray, pieces of guttering, plant trays – if nothing else is available use washing-up bowls or drawer trays and the classroom sink. You will also need a supply of foil containers (the type used to hold small cakes or pies are ideal), some plastic drinking straws, scissors, thin card and a small quantity of Plasticine.

Language to be introduced

Push, blow, fast, slow, blow hard, blow gently, stop, start, change direction, forwards, backwards, sideways, straight.

What to do

Talk to the children about making boats from the foil containers. Initially they can try simply blowing the foil 'boats' across the water. Encourage them to blow against their hands so that they can feel the wind pushing. Suggest hard and soft blowing and get them to describe the different forces. Ask the children:

▲ What happens when you blow the boat?

▲ What is making the boat move along?

▲ Can you make it go faster, slower, change direction?

Later you can introduce the idea of sails made with card. A small length of plastic straw can be used as a mast, held in place with a small blob of Plasticine. As the children blow their little boats, develop their use of the language of forces.

▲ Where is the wind pushing?

▲ Where does your breath have to push to make the boat go backwards?

▲ Can you make your boat travel in a straight line?

▲ Can you make your boat stop?

Some children may develop the idea that the water is pushing against the boat, slowing it down. When the children have explored the way in which the boats move some may be ready to measure or compare distances travelled. This can be recorded by putting marks on a piece of paper laid alongside the water container. Later, this can be turned into a chart.

▲ How far can you make your boat travel with one breath (blow)?

▲ How quickly can you make your boat travel from one end of the container to the other?

▲ Can you see whose boat is faster?

▲ Could you time or count how long your boat takes to go across?

The children could use non-standard measures of time such as counting, or compare two boats travelling at the same time in adjacent containers. It helps to have fairly long stretches of water for this last activity.

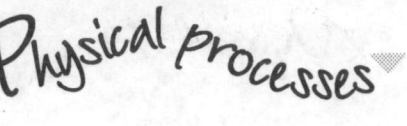

Suggestion(s) for extension

Ask the children what they think would happen if they blew down the plastic straws instead of just blowing with their mouths. Then try it out. Pieces of tubing with different bores would be interesting for comparison, or try moving the boats by flapping newspapers or using battery-powered fans. The learning objective can be reinforced by the investigation of simple mechanical toys, especially toy cars.

Suggestion(s) for support

Younger and less able children may be frustrated by the modelling element of this lesson. If you think your children will not be able to construct a simple sail it would be helpful to prepare some in advance.

Assessment opportunities

Note the children who use the language of forces in the correct contexts and those who devise interesting investigative approaches to answer your questions. Help some of the more able children to suggest fair ways of comparing the performance of their boats with others.

Opportunities for IT

Those children who have made comparisons about the distance travelled could turn their data into a block graph using graphing software. They should be encouraged to interpret the graphs to say which boat went the furthest and give explanations as to why.

Display ideas

The children can draw their boats travelling across the water and add words and arrows to show where the pushes were acting. Those who have compared the boats can make charts of distance travelled by laying paper alongside the water troughs, marking on the distance travelled and cutting strips of paper to length. These can then be displayed as a simple chart.

Other aspects of the Science PoS covered

Experimental and Investigative Science – various aspects of this will be covered depending on the individual teacher's approach.

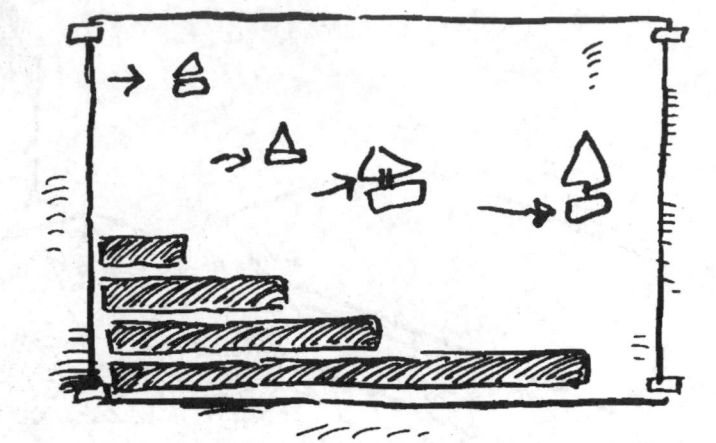

SQUEEZE, SQUASH AND PUMMEL

Forces can change the shape of objects.
†† *Individual work (limited by the availability of resources).*
🕐 *30 minutes.*

Previous skills/knowledge needed

It would be helpful if children had used the language of forces in different contexts (see lessons on pages 74 and 75 of this chapter for ideas).

Preparation

Prepare the working surfaces in the classroom and set out the resources. If comparisons are going to be made between the children's 'clay sausages' it is important that the clay is cut into roughly even-sized portions.

Resources needed

Each child will need a quantity of either salt dough, Plasticine or clay, an apron, a clay board (or some other suitable surface for rolling), access to a rolling pin and other objects to use with the clay. These latter objects should provide opportunities for the creation of pressing patterns so try to include objects which will push into the clay rather than those which will cut it. A recipe for salt dough is given on the photocopiable sheet on page 157.

Language to be introduced

Push, pull, squeeze, squash, roll, press, twist.

What to do

Ask the children to investigate what happens when they push and pull their clay (or other medium). Introduce the idea that all of their pushing, pulling, pressing and rolling has the same basic effect – it changes the shape of the material.

▲ What happens when you push, pull or twist your clay?

▲ Can you squash it so it is thin?

▲ Can you make a bendy or twisted shape?

Now get everyone to roll their material into a ball and set them one or more challenges:

▲ Who can make the longest sausage?

▲ Who can make the thinnest dough without it breaking?

▲ Who can make the twistiest shape?

Talk to the children about the tools:

▲ Do the tools help you to work the clay?

▲ How do they help?

▲ What is making your piece of clay change shape?

Some children may be able to create patterns in their clay. All the various shapes and patterns made can be retained as a record of the activity.

Suggestion(s) for extension

Older and more able children can measure or compare the completed sausage shapes and use the results to make a simple chart. More able children could also try reproducing the patterns made in the clay on paper.

Children with experience of salt dough, clay and Plasticine may be able to talk about the different forces required to mould each material.

The idea of rolling the sausage shape can be extended into the making of coil pots.

Children who have mastered the language introduced so far can have the concept of 'crushing' explained to them. This could be done by making crushed paper pictures or by crushing cans for recycling.

Suggestion(s) for support

Very young children may need considerable reinforcement of the ideas in this lesson. The activities can be carried out over a longer period of time with opportunities to repeat the same activities using each medium (clay, salt dough, Plasticine) in turn.

Assessment opportunities

Note those children who use the language of forces in the appropriate contexts. The questions listed in the 'What to do' section should help you.

Display ideas

The completed 'models' and other results of the use of the clay will stand as evidence. These can be labelled:

'How did Millie make her long sausage shape?'

'Could Ramu have squashed his dough any thinner?'

Photographs of the children pushing, pulling and twisting the dough could be useful for subsequent language development and display.

Other aspects of the Science PoS covered

Materials and their Properties – 2a.

LIGHT AND REFLECTION

Light comes from a variety of sources.

†† *Small-group practical followed by individual worksheets.*

🕑 *45 minutes.*

⚠ *Children should be taught that it is dangerous to look directly at a bright light source, especially the sun.*

Previous skills/knowledge needed

The following activities require an ability to handle fragile objects. Some experience of handling and sorting collections of materials would be useful and the children must have handled the two collections (see below) separately before attempting to use them together. The children will also need to have handled torches before or they will just play with them. If you are introducing torches for the first time you may like to spend some time playing 'torch-tag' or 'mirror-tag', allowing the children to use their own torch or mirror to 'chase' someone else's beam as it is shone around the ceiling. It would be helpful if children had already experienced lighting bulbs (see page 71). This lesson can easily be extended to provide several weeks' work.

Preparation

Collection 1

Make a collection of shiny objects. (This works well at Christmas or when studying other festivals.) The collection could include: decorations, spoons, plastic mirrors (plane, concave or convex), foil papers and gift-wrap, kitchen pots and pans, reflective strips, fluorescent clothing.

Collection 2

Make a separate collection of light sources. This could include: torches, OHP, slide projector, batteries and bulbs, bicycle lights and table lamps.

Either or both of these collections could be put together with the help of the children. The collection of shiny objects makes a lovely display and is worth preparing a few weeks in advance of this lesson to allow children the opportunity to explore it and enjoy their own reflections.

Resources needed

A collection of shiny objects and a collection of light sources. The photocopiable sheet on page 145 can be used as an assessment activity for older and more able children.

Language to be introduced

Shine, shiny, beam, reflection, reflecting, bright, sparkle, surface, reflectors.

What to do

Talk to the children about light and light sources. Make sure they have realised that daylight comes from the sun and that it is dangerous to look directly at the sun. Now introduce the first collection and ask the children what they can see in the shiny objects. Hold some of the collection up to the light and ask the children to describe what they see:
▲ What do you see in this shiny object?
▲ Can you see yourself?
▲ What else can you see?

Now introduce a light source from the second collection to accentuate the reflections. Try holding a piece of tinsel in the beam of a projector or ask a group of children to shine torches in a mirror. Ask them to describe the way the light shines on the object.

Make a point of showing and asking the children to investigate where the light is coming from and (if possible) where it is going (from the light source to their eyes). Try shining a beam from a projector in a partly-darkened room and ask the children where the beam is going. Allow the children time to carry out their own investigations using torches, mirrors and other reflective surfaces. Keep raising questions and responding to their own suggestions for investigation:

▲ Where is the light coming from?
▲ How could we make it sparkle even more?
▲ Do you think it would sparkle like this if we were in a room that was completely dark?
▲ Which surfaces will it reflect off?
▲ What kinds of surfaces make the best reflectors?

As a concluding activity bring all the children together and ask them to sort a jumbled mixture of the two collections into light sources and reflectors.

As a recording activity children can draw what they see reflected in the shiny objects. Older or more able children may get the idea that beams of light can be drawn and this could lead to art work based on beams, sparkles and reflections.

Suggestion(s) for extension

Use the Investigation on 'Light' (page 90).

Suggestion(s) for support

Younger and less able children can be started on this theme by using a collection of spoons. They can look at their own reflections in the concave and convex surfaces and suggest reasons why they can see themselves reflected in some spoons and not in others. Be sure to include a good range of different spoons such as plastic, wooden, slotted, etc. Include some concave or convex mirrors with the collection to aid investigation. This collection provides plenty of opportunity for sorting, measuring, comparing and close observational drawing.

Assessment opportunities

Note those children who can/cannot use the ideas of light source and reflector in the appropriate contexts. Some children will have their own ideas about the way in which light travels and the way in which we see. Make a note of those who have their own ideas and can back them up with evidence of what they have observed. You may also wish to note the level of sophistication of the investigations carried out by individual children using the mirrors and torches. Either use the photocopiable sheet as an assessment task or provide pictures cut from magazines to carry out a sorting activity into light sources and reflectors.

Opportunities for IT

Children could use a prepared concept keyboard overlay linked to a word processor to record their understanding of light sources and reflectors. Pictures of a range of light sources and reflectors could be linked to the appropriate words to make sentences such as 'a candle is a light source'. This could be used after the practical work to assess children's understanding in a simple and interesting way.

Display ideas

The collection of shiny things makes a good display which can be labelled by the teacher to provide language extension for the children. Alternatively, the collection could be labelled by the children themselves to show the various ways in which it can be sorted.

Other aspects of the Science PoS covered

Life Processes and Living Things – 1b, 2f.

Reference to photocopiable sheet

The photocopiable sheet on page 145 can be used immediately after the activity to reinforce the learning objective, or at a later date to assess the children's retained knowledge. Ask pupils to colour or put a ring round the pictures of light sources. To give extra reinforcement, they could also cross out the ones that are not.

MAKING SHADOWS

Darkness is the absence of light.

👥 *Whole class with group practical activities.*

🕐 *45 minutes.*

⚠ *The children must be told not to look directly at the sun.*

Previous skills/knowledge needed

This lesson can be used either before or after the lesson on reflections (page 79). The amount of preparation for the activity will vary accordingly to the children's previous experience, and their familiarity with the language.

Preparation

Some of the suggested activities require access to an area outdoors on a sunny day. This means that parts of the lesson are very difficult to plan in advance and you may need to grasp an opportunity when it arises!

Make a shadow theatre screen by suspending a sheet from the ceiling or fit one over a box or similar framework.

Resources needed

Access to some playground chalk and some rounders posts or other poles would be useful outside. Large sheets of paper and crayons will be needed if you wish to use the shadow drawings as part of a display.

For the indoor part of the lesson you will need a strong light source such as an OHP or slide projector. You will also need a white sheet to act as a screen.

A large, heavy counterpane or very dark sheet could also be useful.

Language to be introduced

Light, shadow, dark, darkness, sun, sunshine, underground, pitch black, night, day, cellar, tunnel, blocking out.

What to do

Talk to the children about the sun and about day and night. Ask them what happens where there is no light and discuss ways in which we light up the darkness in our homes and streets:

▲ Where does our light come from?

▲ What do we call the time when the sun is out/not out?

▲ Is it completely dark/black at night?

▲ What gives us light at night?

Take the children outside and look for shadows. You can draw around some if you like and come back later (perhaps every half hour) to see how they have altered. The rounders posts will act as good shadow sticks or the children could draw around their own shadows. Draw these on sheets of paper if you want to use them for display, otherwise they can be drawn in chalk directly on to the playground.

Play 'shadow-tag', with the children jumping on each

other's shadows. Help the children to realise that a shadow is caused by an object blocking out a little bit of sunshine. See if the children can explain how shadows are made, or describe in what way a shadow is like darkness.

Back in the classroom talk to the children about darkness again and introduce places that are dark in the daytime, such as cupboards, cellars, tunnels and mines. Discuss why this is so. Drape the heavy counterpane over a table so that a few children can go underneath to see if it is completely dark.

Ask the children to describe what darkness is and what causes it.

Finally, allow some children to make shadows using the light source and screen, reinforcing the idea that the shadows are there because the light has been blocked off.

Suggestion(s) for extension
Older or more able children can use the shadow screen to stage a shadow play on the subject of light. Talk to the children about what might happen if the sun did not come up one morning and help them to turn their ideas into an informative and entertaining script.

Alternatively, some children may be able to compare and measure the sizes of shadows at different times of the day and create a simple chart.

Suggestion(s) for support
Less able and younger children may benefit from more discussion on light and dark. They could create pictures with light and dark colours and draw or paint sunshine and night time.

Assessment opportunities
Note those children who can/cannot express a clear understanding of the concept that darkness is the absence of light.

Opportunities for IT
Children could use the shadow stick measurements to create a block graph, using graphing software to show the change in shadows during the day. If they record their measurements at half-hourly intervals they will have enough to show the variation. Older children could also use the software to turn their graph into a line graph; they could be asked how long they think the shadow would be at times between the measurements, then check readings from the graph.

Display ideas
Display the shadow drawings of the children or the objects in the playground alongside a silhouette of the real object (life size) so that pupils can compare the size of the shadow with the real size. The silhouettes and shadow shapes can be used as a backing for art and written work and include open-ended questions provided by the teacher.

Other aspects of the Science PoS covered
More able children could develop their exploration of shadows into a full investigation.

SOUNDS GOOD!

There are many kinds of sound.

†† *Whole-class or small-group practical.*

🕐 *40 minutes.*

Previous skills/knowledge needed

Some experience of sorting collections of sounds would be helpful. Children should have had the opportunity to handle and explore percussion instruments before this lesson.

Preparation

Write 'sounds' words on cards (see 'Language to be introduced' below). You will need to cover the range of sounds produced by the instruments you are using. With the youngest children picture cards can replace the word cards.

Make a collection of percussion instruments. Sort them into groups of tuned and untuned percussion or, if the children are reasonably familiar with the instruments, they should be able to do this as part of the lesson.

Resources needed

In addition to the collection of percussion instruments you will also need a range of beaters and scrapers. You may like to supplement the collection with other instruments (non-percussion) or increase the variety of sounds by including children's voices and body sounds.

Language to be introduced

Shake, rattle, hit, scrape, scratch, blow, soft, loud, high, low, long, short, bang, crash, crunch, ding, ting, ping, ring, clang, boom. As this list suggests there are many ways of describing sounds which are not 'real' words. As the aim of this lesson is to show that there are many sounds it may be helpful to encourage the children to create their own words for sounds.

What to do

Sit the children in a circle and talk to them about the instruments and the sounds they make. Ask some children to play the instruments and to describe either the sound or the way in which they are making the sound:

▲ This is a loud sound.

▲ This is a scraping sound.

▲ I am making a banging sound.

Encourage a few children to explore the range of sounds which their instrument can produce. Introduce the idea that the instrument may be scraped, tapped, shaken, turned over, and so on.

Help the children to develop their ideas by asking them open-ended questions:

▲ What sounds can you make using this instrument?

Or, if you are using body sounds:

▲ What sounds can you make with your mouth/hands/feet/tongue/voice?

▲ Can you make a loud/soft/high/low/long/short sound?

▲ Can you find a different way of making the same sound?

This activity can be turned into a simple game where each child in turn is asked to remember the sequence of sounds made so far:

▲ Mark made a soft sound.

▲ Ellie made a crunching sound.

▲ Yuri made a high sound.

▲ Now it's your turn.

The word or picture cards can be placed in front of the children who are playing to help them remember.

The game could also be adapted to play 'I went to the *sounds* shop and I bought a .... (and here you make the sound). This builds into a memory game with each player adding a new sound in turn. A similar game could be played by adapting the popular song 'The Music Man' or by using the song on the photocopiable sheet on page 146.

Use the word cards to tell each new player how to play their instrument, or let groups of children play, following the instructions on the cards.

Add further variety by introducing the different types of beater and stretch the children by asking questions such as:

▲ What difference would it make if you used a different beater/used your finger tips/used the side of the instrument?

▲ How would you describe the sound you are making?

▲ How many different sounds can you make?

The children could record their sounds as patterns, as sound pictures or using a tape recorder.

When the instruments have been explored ask pupils to sort the collection. Children will often sort for shape, size and colour, so explain that the sorting this time is to be for sound. If they need help the word cards can act as headings for the sets.

Suggestion(s) for extension

This lesson can be extended by introducing an increasing variety of instruments into the collection. Creative writing can be produced using the children's own sound words. Musical compositions can be practised and performed to show the range of sounds which can be developed from a limited number of instruments. Further extension can be provided by taking the children beyond the range of sounds the instruments can make to sounds created in a wider context. Ask pupils to find sounds in the classroom, or present them with another collection of sound makers such as clay flowerpots or part-filled glass bottles. Tell stories in sounds, including everyday items such as an alarm clock.

Suggestion(s) for support

Less able children may find it hard to cope with a wide range of variables, so use a limited selection of sounds in each single lesson. If in doubt, start with just a few instruments from one section of the collection. The lesson can be repeated many times, introducing different sounds each time.

Assessment opportunities

Concentrate particularly on the sorting activity. This could be done as a separate lesson with a small group or with individual children you wish to assess in more detail. Notice in particular those children who are unable to sort using the sounds as the criteria. Can these children sort according to the way in which the instruments are played? If they are unable to get beyond the criteria of colour, size and shape they may need reinforcement activities. The most able children may suggest the use of pitch or some other musical or aesthetic criteria for sorting.

Opportunities for IT

Older children could work with a simple sound source data base, either prepared by the teacher in advance, or added to by the children themselves. The field names could include:

instrument	*drum*
sound made by	*banging, plucking, blowing*
pitch	*high, low, many*
made from	*wood, metal, plastic*

In order to be consistent children need to decide at the outset which words they are going to use to describe the pitch or what the instrument is made from. Children could explore the completed database asking simple questions like:

▲ How many instruments are made from wood?

▲ Which instruments are played by blowing?

Children might also have opportunities to use CD-ROMs to find out extra information about the instruments in the database, or to explore the actual sounds made by different instruments.

Display ideas

Use a subset of the collection of instruments (such as chime bars) as a display. Add open-ended questions to the display such as:

'Can you put these instruments in order from high sounds to low sounds?'

The 'sounds' words cards and pictures can also be included in your display.

Other 'sound makers' also make good items for display. Flowerpots and/or bottles can be suspended from a simple framework to enhance their sound. The display could also include sound pictures drawn by the children.

Other aspects of the Science PoS covered

Life Processes and Living Things – 2f.

Reference to photocopiable sheet

The photocopiable sheet on page 146 contains a song which you may wish to teach to your class to extend their listening skills and auditory sequencing memory. At the end of each verse, the children take it in turns to repeat the sounds made in the previous verse before adding one of their own. You may wish to have the previous sound makers joining in until the new sound maker makes his or her new sound. Keep the sounds very short; one beat on a drum, one clap of the hands, and so on, and make them as varied as possible until the children are familiar with the song.

SOUNDS ALL AROUND

Different things make different sounds.

†† *Whole-class practical.*

🕐 *60 minutes.*

⚠ *Extra adult supervision may be necessary if you decide to go outside.*

Previous skills/knowledge needed

This lesson builds on children's early listening experiences. The youngest Key Stage 1 children should first complete the lesson called 'Exploring sound' in the 'Life Processes and Living Things' chapter of this book (page 18). Moreover, as the collection used in this lesson is 'abstract' some experience of sorting 'concrete' collections of materials would be very useful. Children will be able to draw on their experience of listening activities from music lessons.

Preparation

Either make your own or use a commercial sound-effects tape for this lesson. If you make your own tape put in a variety of sounds to help the children make a simple chart (see 'What to do' below).

Organise your adult helpers and groups if you intend to go outside and, if possible, have one or more battery-operated portable tape recorders ready to take with you. Walk the intended route by yourself before the lesson. This will give you the opportunity to think about any specific vocabulary which may be necessary. You may wish a few of the more able children to take a clipboard, pencil and paper with them.

As you get ready to start the lesson choose two or three items which will make a noise, and which are small enough to conceal in a bag or under a cloth on your lap.

Resources needed

A range of sound makers which could include: a percussion instrument, an electronic game or alarm, a plastic bottle with a lid (or anything else with a characteristic sound), tape recorders, clipboards, sound-effects tape.

Language to be introduced

The language for this lesson is likely to be drawn from four main categories:

▲ Describing the sound – high/low, soft/loud, short/long, swish, crunch.

▲ Describing how the sound is made – scrape, hit, shake.

▲ Describing the material from which the sound is made – glass, metal, wood, plastic.

▲ Describing what makes the sound – bird, insect, car.

What to do

Talk to the children about sounds: loud sounds, common sounds, animal sounds, town sounds, wooden sounds, voices, etc. Make some sounds under a cover (ask the

---

85

children to close their eyes) and see if the children can identify the sounds. Ask the children:

▲ What do you think makes this sound?

▲ What is the object made of?

▲ How can you tell this?

▲ Can you describe the sound?

Listen to some of the sounds on the tape, then ask the children:

▲ Can you identify the sources of the sounds?

▲ How do you know the sources of the sounds?

▲ What is it about the sound that makes it different from other sounds? (This is difficult but can be very rewarding.)

▲ Where would you usually hear the sound?

▲ What else do you know which makes sounds?

If the children can identify the sounds, you can go on to identify categories for a simple chart. These could be very simple, such as loud and soft, or more complex such as animal/not animal, or metal/wood/plastic/glass. Draw the chart on a large sheet of paper or on a white board. Plan the categories to match the tape you are using.

If the children are able to sustain more work in this lesson listen first to any sounds which you can hear in your classroom, then go out on a listening walk. On your walk record both natural and man-made sounds The sounds collected from these activities can be included on your chart, and new categories added if necessary.

Suggestion(s) for extension

Older or more able children could use their experiences of sound or put together a sounds symphony which illustrates the way in which different things make different sounds. The symphony could include a spoken introduction or narrative running through the sounds.

In addition some children could make their own charts and graphs of the sounds they hear. This could be further extended by giving the children time to listen in different parts of the school and at different times of day.

Suggestion(s) for support

For younger children this lesson could be broken down into its individual components and taught as a series of lessons. If less able children are being taught with the rest of the class you could provide language support by producing picture cards with the relevant vocabulary beside each picture, or ask the children to draw the things which make the sounds. These pictures could be used later to create a game of 'Sounds bingo' in which the children match pictures to pre-recorded sounds on an audio tape.

Assessment opportunities

The learning objective for this lesson can be realised at many different levels. When assessing the children take particular notice of those who can/cannot connect the source of the sound with the *material* from which the object is made and also *how* the sound is made.

Opportunities for IT

The use of the tape recorder gives children opportunities for developing simple control work – start, stop, pause, record – and for saving and retrieving their work. Children could also experiment with the sound synthesizer parts of many modern keyboards.

Display ideas

If you have a set of headphones or a group listening centre you can make this the focus of a sounds display. Use the chart created during the lesson to act as a stimulus for questions, some of which can be displayed alongside the chart, such as:

▲ What makes these sounds?

▲ How many sounds are made by metal things?

▲ Where did we hear most sounds?

▲ What is the most common sound?

The children can make their own tapes of sounds and use them to create a listening quiz on a tape recorder as part of an interactive display.

Other aspects of the Science PoS covered

Materials and their Properties – 1a, 1b, 1c, 1d, 1e.
Life Processes and Living Things – 2f.

SOUND MOVES

Sound travels out from its source getting fainter as it goes.

†† *Group practical activity or whole-class session, followed by group work.*

🕐 *40 minutes.*

⚠ *Some additional adult support may be necessary if you decide to go outside. A different approach may be necessary for children who are hearing impaired.*

Previous skills/knowledge needed

Some experience of listening activities is essential.

Preparation

Have the musical instruments ready and set out the paper, paints and pots ready to create the splatter pictures.

Resources needed

You will need a small snare drum (or equivalent) scattered with small seeds or lentils to demonstrate vibration, a stringed instrument such as a guitar, several small pots (sandwich paste pots are suitable) filled with coloured water, a few musical tuning forks (one per group), large sheets of sugar paper.

If you choose to do the outside part of the lesson you will also need some musical instruments to make sounds over a range of distances. Try a chime bar, cymbals or a drum. A portable, battery-powered, electronic keyboard would be very useful; timpani and a double bass are optional extras!

Language to be introduced

Tuning fork, vibration, movement, moving, travel, travelling, listen, hear, sound.

What to do

Talk to the children about what they hear. Discuss the fact that they can hear things from a long way away:

▲ What can you hear if you listen carefully now?

▲ Can you hear anything which is a long way away?

▲ What would the sound be like if we were closer to it?

Show the children that sound can make things move. Do this by sprinkling small seeds or lentils on to the surface of a snare drum. Tap the top skin of the drum and watch the seeds jump about. Ask the children to predict what will happen if the bottom skin of the drum is tapped.

Introduce the idea that to make a sound there must be some kind of movement or vibration. This can be shown with the seeds on the drum or with a guitar string. It is also possible to *feel* the vibration and, if you have access to a large stringed instrument or drum, the feeling can be quite dramatic.

It is difficult to show that sound travels, but it is relatively easy to show that vibration makes things move. For some children this may be a step towards understanding the movement of sound.

Use one of the tuning forks to show that the ends of the fork move when it makes a sound, so that when there is sound there is movement. A more spectacular way of showing the movement of a tuning fork is to dip the vibrating end of the fork into a small pot of water. (Fill the pot to the absolute brim.) The water will then be sprayed by the vibration. Ask the children:

▲ Can you see the tuning fork moving/vibrating?

▲ What will happen if I put the end of the fork in this water?

▲ What is making the water move?

The resulting splatter picture could be used to represent the way in which vibration makes the air move but this is a difficult concept and not one which is worth exploring in detail at Key Stage 1.

At this point give the children the opportunity to make their own splatter/vibration pictures.

If the children are able to sustain more activity in this lesson take them outside, or to a quiet hall, so that they can listen to sounds travelling towards them. First, ask the children to listen for sounds which they think are coming from a long way away. Get them to turn their heads towards the different sounds they can hear to help identify the direction the sounds are coming from. This will help reinforce the idea that the sound is entering their ears.

Next, use a musical instrument to test from what distance the children can hear a particular sound. Ask them to stand in a line with their backs to you. Walk a little distance away and ask the children to put up their hands when they can/ cannot hear the sound. (Try it both ways.) The portable electronic keyboard is useful here as it gives a constant note at a constant volume. This activity often gives rise to a great deal of discussion about fair testing. There are always children in the class who can hear *everything!*

Back in the classroom, the children can draw themselves taking part in this listening activity.

Suggestion(s) for extension
As extension material use the investigation outlined in the chapter 'Investigations' in this book (see page 91). The school's audiometric nurse may be able to talk to the children about the way in which she or he tests hearing.

Suggestion(s) for support
For young children this lesson can be split into its component parts and taught over a longer period of time to allow opportunities for questioning and reflection. Some children may also need additional practical experience to help them develop the concept of vibration and sound. For these

children it would be best to reinforce the ideas through additional activities such as making string telephones (feel the vibrations on the string) and making simple musical instruments like an elastic band guitar.

Assessment opportunities
Ask the children to draw themselves listening to sounds and see if they can represent the sound in some way within the picture. Talk to the children about their pictures and ask them open-ended questions (like those that have been asked during the course of the lesson) to assess their level of understanding.

Display ideas
Display the children's sound pictures with the splatter/ vibration pictures as a background.

Other aspects of the Science PoS covered
Life Processes and Living Things – 2f.

Investigations

Children have a natural desire to investigate. The teacher's task is to help pupils develop a structure for this natural curiosity through the development of scientific skills.

Most young children need to start with the practical experience of obtaining evidence. This is best done by the creation of collections of materials. Through the practical activity of handling, observing and measuring these collections children begin to interpret their world and order their thoughts to produce questions which can be investigated.

It is important for children to be given every opportunity to follow their own suggestions for investigation and to reach their own conclusions. Many of the activities in the following lessons are open-ended so that children can develop their skills as real scientists.

The photocopiable sheet on page 150 may help pupils to structure their approach to these investigations.

Investigation is the core of all scientific work and every child will need considerable practice before being able to apply these skills confidently and independently.

Children should always be developing their investigative skills when engaged in science activities. The lessons in this chapter draw on the content areas of the National Curriculum for Science, demonstrating how investigations can be developed with young children.

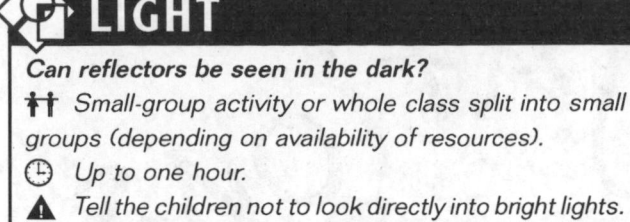

LIGHT

Can reflectors be seen in the dark?

👥 *Small-group activity or whole class split into small groups (depending on availability of resources).*

🕐 *Up to one hour.*

⚠️ *Tell the children not to look directly into bright lights.*

Previous skills/knowledge needed

Pupils should have covered the work included in the 'Light and reflection' lesson on page 79.

Key background information

Light comes from a light source and this is then reflected off objects in its path. We see an object because the light reflected from that object enters our eyes.

Preparation

Collect shoe boxes and other resources listed below. Immediately before the lesson prepare a dark area where the children can sit. If you have a part of the school which has a good blackout this is ideal, but this lesson will work, even if you cannot create blackout conditions. If at all possible, start the lesson sitting in a darkened room with a strong light source (a slide projector or a powerful torch) switched on. This situation may help the children generate ideas for the investigation to follow. Alternatively, you may be able to create a dark place in your classroom by throwing a heavy cloth over a table and allowing a few children at a time to sit underneath it.

Resources needed

A collection of reflective materials (include shiny papers, bicycle reflectors, road safety clothing strips, Christmas decorations, plastic mirrors), a variety of small light sources (such as torches and bicycle lamps).

Boxes with lids can be used to create dark places in which to put the reflective materials. Shoe boxes are ideal. Punch a *little* hole in one end of each box to act as a spy hole.

What to do

Look at the various reflectors and light sources in your collection and encourage the children to sort the items into the two categories of 'Reflectors' and 'Light sources'.

Ask the children which items will shine in the dark.

They will probably have experience of items from both groups shining in the dark. You need to be aware of what the children understand by 'shine' and 'dark' in order to decide if a child's answer is acceptable. More able children may try to define these words at this point. 'It will shine if something shines on it,' is a common observation from older children.

Encourage the children to think about complete darkness, but first check that they have a clear concept of darkness. Can they describe what total darkness is like? Have they ever been anywhere where it is completely dark?

At this point the children may come up with an idea of their own for testing which is slightly different from the one you have prepared. If at all possible allow the children to follow their own line of investigation. The main criterion for rejecting a child's own suggestion is that you know it will provide an unsatisfactory learning experience for that child. This will depend on the individual so professional judgement must be used.

In the event that no good suggestions are made, investigate this idea:

Can reflectors be seen in the dark?

Once an idea for testing has been established, the children will need time for planning. Ask them:

▲ What are you going to do?

▲ Can you tell me/draw a picture to show me?

▲ How will your idea prove it one way or the other?

The children will already have gained considerable evidence for their views from previous work with the collection of materials and light sources. Now it is time for them to gather evidence which is specific to the idea being tested. Some children may want to seek out complete darkness, but this is very difficult (and potentially dangerous). Try the darkened room or sitting under a darkened table, but if some children continue to be dissatisfied with their test conditions introduce the shoe boxes.

Show the children that they can create a darkened space within a shoe box. Can they think how the box could be used to test their ideas? The amount of guidance required will vary according to the age and ability of pupils, but let the children decide for themselves as much as possible. One likely outcome is that the items from the collection could be placed one at a time into the far end of the box (away from the hole). The children will then look through the hole to see if the items are giving out light.

Be careful that the children do not feel that they have to prove that their own idea is right to the exclusion of all others. It is all too easy for any scientist to see what she or he wants to see and prove what she or he wants to prove. Objectivity is an important factor, so ask:

▲ How can you check to see if your answer is right?

▲ Is that fair?

▲ Would it be the same for everyone?

▲ What would happen if we did it again and asked someone else?

▲ Do you think that adults would give the same answer?

The children will then need help to consider the evidence they have gathered:

▲ What have you found out so far?

▲ What else do you need to do? Why?

▲ Have you been surprised by anything you have seen?

▲ Have you changed your mind about anything?

▲ What have you learned?

Encourage children to compare their findings with those of others in the class.

Suggestion(s) for extension

More able children could record their observations, perhaps as a simple tick chart. The photocopiable sheet on page 124 may be helpful.

Suggestion(s) for support

Those children who are unable to sustain the open-ended format of this investigation are probably not ready to handle complete investigations. They should be given more opportunity to sort and classify the collection of materials, and perhaps to record the similarities and differences which they identify through a variety of artistic media.

Assessment opportunities

Take particular note of the children who can/cannot generate interesting and original ideas for investigation, discover solutions to the practical problems which arise during testing, and summarise their findings in terms of what they have observed.

Display ideas

To draw the investigation to a conclusion, the children should be encouraged to present their findings to others. This can be done by creating a display of the children's completed charts, drawings and writing which can accompany the collection of materials and other items used in the investigation.

Other aspects of the Science PoS covered

Physical Processes – 3b.

SOUND

How far away can you hear a sound?

†† *Whole-class introduction with small group investigations to follow.*

🕑 *Up to one hour.*

⚠ *Extra adult help may be necessary as some groups may need to go outside or to a hall or corridor space.*

Key background information

Sound travels out from its source in all directions, getting fainter as it travels. Whether a child says he or she can or cannot hear a sound will depend on a complex series of variables which could include the child's ability to concentrate, identify the sound, hear at the pitch being generated, be honest, and the amount of background noise.

Preparation

Some investigators may ask for blindfolds, in an attempt to stop children pretending to hear sounds when they don't! Other children may devise a system where the listeners walk away from the sound until they can't hear it any more. This group may require cones or markers to place where the children stop hearing the sound. Have the blindfolds ready to hand and put a supply of cones outside. Pre-record a constant sound on a cassette tape or provide a portable

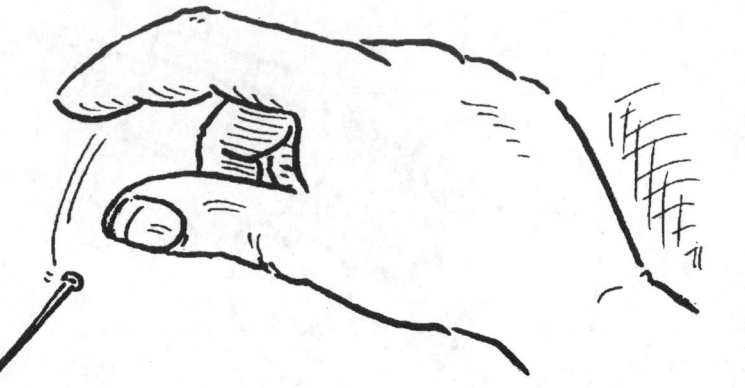

electronic keyboard. Plan your pupil groups with the need for cooperative group work in mind and remember that the purpose of this investigation is not to seek the definitive scientific answer to the idea being investigated but rather to provide each child with experience of being a scientific investigator.

Resources needed

Blindfolds, marker cones (mentioned above), long tape-measures or lengths of string, a pin, and a variety of surfaces on which it can be dropped such as a tin lid, a carpet square, a plastic box or a chime bar, a pre-recorded sound on a tape or a portable electronic keyboard, clipboards, paper, pencils.

Language to be introduced

Loud, soft, quiet, faint, measure, fair test, sound.

What to do

Talk to the children about sounds and how we hear them. If they are familiar with the saying 'You could hear a pin drop' you may like to discuss what the saying means and give the children a chance to say whether or not they can hear a pin drop. Drop a pin on to a metal surface such as a tin lid and ask the children to put their hands up if they can hear the sound. Then ask them to close their eyes and repeat this. On a third occasion, ask them to close their eyes and do not drop the pin. Tell them what you did and point out that they need to be honest every time. Change the surface on to which you are dropping the pin and try again.

Check that the children have a clear understanding of the fact that sound travels away from its source and gets fainter as it goes.

▲ Could you hear the pin drop from the other side of the room?

▲ Does it make a difference where you stand or sit when the pin is dropped?

▲ What else might make a difference?

Tell the children that they are going to test to find out:

How far away can you hear a sound?

Once the idea to be tested has been established the children should be given some time for planning. Show them the resources which are available to them and ask them to think about and discuss for a short time how they will find out the answer to the question. This initial planning can be done in small groups, as pairs or as individuals, according to the children's age and ability. However, the actual investigation will require cooperative work in small groups.

When the children have had a while to think their ideas through and discuss them you can ask them:

▲ How could we find out how far away we can hear the sound?

▲ What would we have to do?

▲ Can we do that?

▲ Where would it be best to carry out the investigations?

▲ Are you allowed to go there?

▲ What exactly are you going to do?

▲ Can you tell me/draw a picture to show me?

When carrying out their investigations encourage the children to try each test more than once and explain that sometimes we can be mistaken about what we hear.

The long tape-measures and lengths of string can be used to measure or compare distances within and between different groups. Then ask the children:

▲ Does everyone hear the same?

▲ What have you found out so far?

▲ Do you think your results are right?

▲ Have you been as fair as you can?

▲ Is there another way you could try it?

▲ Would you get the same answer if you tried the test with a different sound/note?

▲ How else could you check your findings?

Once the children have completed their investigation they should be given the opportunity to consider the evidence they have collected and compare it with other groups.

Suggestion(s) for extension

If you have a tape recorder with headphones it may be possible for some children to set up a test to see if they hear equally well with each ear.

Suggestion(s) for support

The ideas in this lesson can be broken down into parts for children who find the process of investigation difficult. The teacher should continue to carry out the testing, using a simple test, such as everyone walking away from the teacher until they can no longer hear the sound.

Assessment opportunities

Take particular note of those children who suggest that using chime bars and other percussion instruments may not be fair. Also check the level of sophistication of the ideas put forward for investigation. For instance older and more able children might suggest that it may be different for different people, and may subsequently suggest trying the same sound for a number of different individuals.

Display ideas

This investigation lends itself to a frieze-style display in which different children are illustrated at different points along the wall. Care must be taken to ensure that no individuals feel that they are being 'shown up'. Alternatively, display the variety of testing ideas generated by the children.

Other aspects of the Science PoS covered

Physical Processes – 3d.

BIRDS

Which food do birds like best?
†† *Whole class with subsequent individual or group work.*
🕑 *This is a long-term study and the children should become involved in feeding the birds several weeks before the investigation itself. Pupils will need to undertake more than one period of observation in order to complete the investigation.*
▲ *Be aware of the health and hygiene implications of handling and storing food in the classroom. Use rodent-proof containers for nuts and seeds, and ensure that pupils wash their hands thoroughly after they have handled bird feeders and water containers.*

Previous skills/knowledge needed

Children should have some previous experience of bird watching, bird identification and know that different species of birds eat different foods.

Key background information

You will need to consider the moral issues surrounding investigations on wildlife as wild birds will come to rely on feeding stations and bird tables. Once you start feeding the birds you should continue to do so until plentiful natural sources of food are available to them. This continuity of feeding is especially important in schools, so that young children learn that it is not acceptable to experiment on the natural world in a thoughtless way. It may be helpful to discuss the way in which we look after pets at home. We would not go away and leave our pets to starve. It would also be wrong to let the birds go hungry over a holiday period.

The best time to begin feeding birds is in January, continuing throughout the Spring Term. Peanuts should not be included in the feed once the first nestlings have hatched. Stop feeding at the end of the Spring Term.

Preparation

Order your bird cake mixture and peanuts from a supplier exhibiting the 'We're Safe Nuts' symbol. Store them in rodent-proof containers like those used in school kitchens. Ask the children to bring in a supply of meat fats and bacon rinds or buy suet from a local butcher.

Buy appropriate food dispensers for the food you intend using (peanut holders, seed holders, suet holders) and plan with the children where it would be best to site them. Consider the following factors:
▲ How easily can the feeders be seen from the classroom or other observation point?
▲ Will the feeding birds be at risk from predators or too easily disturbed by other children, traffic, and so on?
▲ Can the feeders be easily refilled when empty?
▲ Is there cover nearby for the birds to use as perches before coming to the feeders?

As the different feeders are going to be compared it is also important that they are situated close to one another.

Let the children help you to make bird cake (see the photocopiable sheet on page 147) then hang this near the other feeders or place it as a block on a bird table. Feed the birds for several weeks until you get a range of regular visitors. Encourage the children to watch for feeding birds and help them identify one or two common ones. You could even prepare part of your classroom as a hide – black out a window or windows with sheets of sugar paper and cut holes (either slits or portholes) in the paper for the children to use as viewing points.

Resources needed
Bird food and feeders, copies of the photocopiable sheet on page 148.

What to do
Talk to the children about the birds which visit the feeders and what they like to eat. Ask them if they have noticed any patterns in the way the birds visit the feeders.
▲ Which food do you think the blue tits like best? Why?
▲ Which birds do we see most often eating the bird cake?
▲ How often do these birds come?
▲ Do they have special times for coming? When are these?
▲ Which food do you think the birds like best?

Tell the children that they are going to carry out an investigation to try to find out:

Which food do birds like best?
Ask questions such as:
▲ Do you have any ideas on how you could find this out?
▲ What will you need to do?
▲ What will you need to help you?
▲ Who will you need to help you?

The children could write a plan of action at this stage, or you may prefer to note those children with good ideas and develop them orally with the whole class.

The children, depending on their age and ability, may need to be led to a reasonable means of answering the question. Some children may come up with their own way of finding the answer. If this happens, and you feel that their idea will give them a satisfactory learning experience, they should, if possible, be allowed to follow their ideas through and carry out their own investigation. If the children do not come up with any workable ideas use a frequency chart (see the photocopiable sheet on page 148).

Try using the frequency sheet with the whole class for a short time to show them how it works. Decide how long each observation period will be and put a tick for every bird visiting the feeder during this time.

Check that the children understand the idea of the frequency chart and ask them how they think the ticks will help to answer the question, 'Which food do birds like best?'.

Suggestion(s) for extension
To create a more demanding frequency chart put the names of birds across the top and descriptions of the bird feeders down the side. More able children should be able to organise observation in groups, with each child responsible for filling in a particular part or parts of the sheet.

More able and older children can take the tally of ticks from the frequency charts and turn the results into a chart of daily visits.

Some children could be allowed to use binoculars.

Suggestion(s) for support
To help younger children become familiar with the characteristics of particular species of birds do not use the accepted name but give them a chance to describe the bird first. From this you may get 'blue head' (blue tit), 'shiny wing' (starling), and so on.

Assessment opportunities
The key issue in this lesson is to assess whether or not the children are able to come up with their own suggestions as to how the investigation should proceed and justify (to their own satisfaction) that they have reached an acceptable conclusion.

These factors are best assessed through conversation

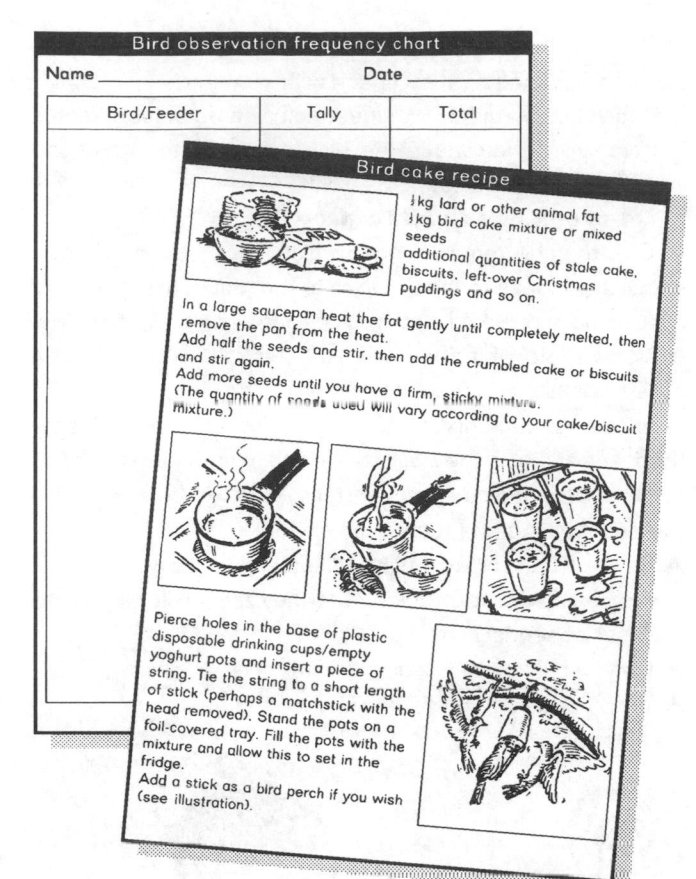

Bird observation frequency chart

Name _____ Date _____

Bird/Feeder	Tally	Total

Bird cake recipe

½ kg lard or other animal fat
½ kg bird cake mixture or mixed seeds
additional quantities of stale cake, biscuits, left-over Christmas puddings and so on.

In a large saucepan heat the fat gently until completely melted, then remove the pan from the heat.
Add half the seeds and stir, then add the crumbled cake or biscuits and stir again.
Add more seeds until you have a firm, sticky mixture.
(The quantity of seeds used will vary according to your cake/biscuit mixture.)

Pierce holes in the base of plastic disposable drinking cups/empty yoghurt pots and insert a piece of string. Tie the string to a short length of stick (perhaps a matchstick with the head removed). Stand the pots on a foil-covered tray. Fill the pots with the mixture and allow this to set in the fridge.
Add a stick as a bird perch if you wish (see illustration).

with the individuals concerned or when listening to the children talk as they present their ideas to the rest of the class. To allow assessment to take place, every child needs to have the opportunity to express her or his ideas. Allow plenty of time for feedback and summary sessions – these can take place at the end of the final period of observation each day, or immediately after each group has completed its turn at observing. Make sure that children who are more reticent than others about expressing their ideas in public still have the opportunity to explain their thinking.

Display ideas
A display-sized copy of the tally totals from the observation sheet can be displayed alongside a large chart of the results.

Other aspects of the Science PoS covered
Life Processes and Living Things – 1b, 4b, 5a.

Reference to photocopiable sheets
The photocopiable sheet on page 147 provides a simple recipe for bird cake, which can be made with, or without, the children's help.

The photocopiable sheet on page 148 is a chart on which children can record the number of birds visiting each feeder. Put a picture, or a description of one of the feeders in each column, or use the more demanding method given in 'Suggestions for extension'.

SEEDS

Do seeds need soil to grow?
†† *Whole class in groups.*
🕐 *45 minutes to prepare (but several weeks in total if growing time is included).*
⚠ *Use seeds that have not been dressed with insecticide. Warn young children not to put seeds in their ears, nostrils and mouths.*

Previous skills/knowledge needed
Children will achieve a higher degree of independence when carrying out this investigation if they have planted seeds on a previous occasion. In any case, the children attempting this investigation will need to have a basic understanding that plants have certain needs in order to grow, such as light and water (they do not need a complete understanding of all the factors involved in plant growth). See the lesson on page 35 for ideas.

Key background information
Plant the seeds at the beginning of a week so that the children will have the opportunity to see the seeds begin to germinate. If seeds are planted on a Thursday some of the initial excitement can be lost if germination takes place quickly (given the right conditions) and the first growth takes place over the weekend.

Preparation
Collect a variety of containers for seed trays and a variety of growing media. Buy seeds which are quick to germinate (consider first whether you wish the children to have a variety of seed types or just one or two different ones). Mustard, cress and grass are all suitable, as well as many small vegetable seeds and the traditional bean. If working with a limited range of seed types use grass seed (because grass is so well known to the children and they don't often think

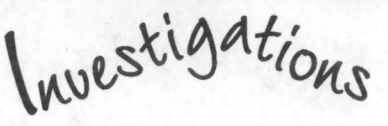
about it having seeds) or mustard or cress (because they can be eaten). If trying a wide range of seeds it is worth asking parents for contributions as most people don't use a whole packet of vegetable seeds at one time.

Clear a space big enough for the seed trays to be stored and monitored. Immediately before the lesson put the seeds to be used in sealed containers, such as margarine tubs, and place the containers with the other resources on the tables for each group. Keep the water pots in reserve as otherwise you may find that the children water the seeds before thinking the investigation through.

Resources needed

Small trays to act as seed trays (if possible collect a large number of trays which are similar in size and shape as this will remove one of the variables in the investigation), cotton wool, compost, blotting paper (and/or other papers such as paper towels, tissue, newspaper), soil from the local environment, a small container of water for each group, copies of the photocopiable sheet on page 149.

set out on the table, and other things from around the classroom, providing they check with you first.

If the children did not suggest soil as a necessary factor in plant growth introduce the idea now, and tell them the idea they will be testing is:

Do seeds need soil to grow?

Give the children a chance to plan what they will do and explain their ideas to the group or to the rest of the class. Try not to impose one rigid methodology and allow pupils to follow their own line of thinking if you think it will provide a satisfactory learning experience for the children involved.

Encourage the children to think about how they will sow the seeds and how they will care for them afterwards. Check to make sure that they understand they will be answering the idea that is being tested, by asking:

▲ How will that tell us if plants need soil to grow?

Also ask them to predict what they think will happen to each set of seeds:

▲ Do you think they will all grow?

▲ Which ones do you think will grow the best?

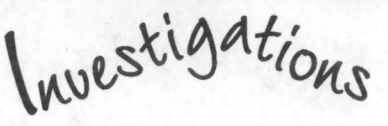

What to do

Talk to the children about seeds and what they are. Ask them:

▲ Do you know what seeds are?

▲ What makes seeds begin to grow?

▲ What things do plants need to grow?

▲ How do we care for classroom plants?

Use the opportunity to remind the children about seeds they have seen before. They may have emptied a pumpkin, or grown sunflowers. They should all be familiar with seeds in fruit.

Send the children, in groups, to their tables and ask them to look at the seeds in the pots. Ask them to describe the seeds and compare them, but not to mix them up. Warn them that seeds are sometimes poisonous.

If the children have already identified 'soil' as one of the things a plant needs to grow ask them to consider how they could prove this. Tell them that they can use the resources

Once the seeds have been planted, and the children have agreed a good place to put them, bring everyone back together again and discuss how the seeds are going to be watched and their progress monitored. The photocopiable sheet on page 149 may help with this.

Suggestion(s) for extension

Some older and more able children may be able to grasp the idea that planting two or three pots with the same seeds and growing medium will give a more reliable result than just planting one. They may also identify other variables and suggest ways of making the test more fair. Sometimes this will involve planting a second set of seed trays, so keep a few seeds in reserve.

Suggestion(s) for support

With younger and less able children break the investigation

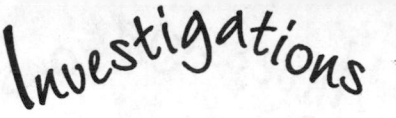
into its component parts and provide more support, in the form of teacher input, at each stage. With these children you should start with one type of seed and one growing medium, gradually adding different media until the testing procedure has been firmly established. You can then let the children do their own investigation, repeating the pattern which you have established.

Assessment opportunities
Make a note of those children who need a great deal of support to design the test, and those who are full of their own ideas about how to set the investigation in motion. Check to see who can relate their explanations to actual events and observations by saying things such as 'I believe... because I saw ....'.

Display ideas
This investigation provides potential for a good display. Surround the seed trays with questions about growing seeds and, as a centrepiece, write the idea to be tested. Include pupils' plans for the investigation and predictions of what they think will happen.

Other aspects of the Science PoS covered
Life and Living Processes – 3a, 3b, 3c.

Reference to photocopiable sheet
The photocopiable sheet on page 149 is a seed growing record sheet. Ask the children to note the variety of seeds and the date on which the seeds were planted. They can then use the boxes to record the growth of the seeds.

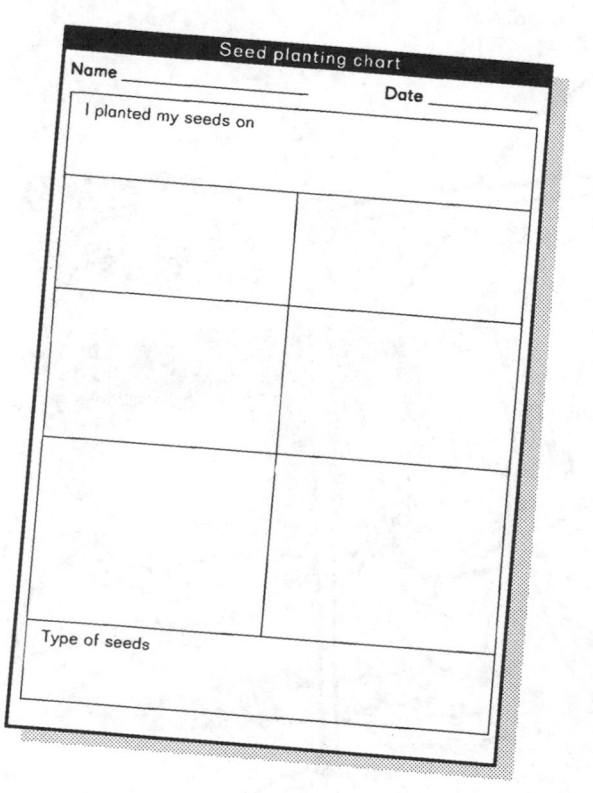

⚙ ABSORBENCY

Which material is best for mopping up spills?
†† *Whole class working in groups.*
🕐 *40 minutes.*

Previous skills/knowledge needed
No special skills or previous knowledge are required but the investigation may be enhanced if the children have already explored absorbent materials as part of free-play activities in the water tray.

Preparation
Collect a variety of cloths and other absorbent materials commonly used to mop up spills. Provide a small container as a means of 'spilling' a measured or constant amount of water.

Resources needed
A range of absorbent cloths (which could include J-cloths, supermarket general purpose cloths or dusters), absorbent paper (paper towels, kitchen roll, newspaper or tissue), a small container for water (egg cup, measuring cylinder or syringe). You could also include some non-absorbent materials to act as a contrast.

What to do
Talk to the children about the collection of cloths and other resources.
▲ Do you know what they are used for?
▲ Do you use any of these at home?
▲ Which ones do you use?
▲ Which are used in school?
▲ Why do different people use different ones?
▲ Why do some people prefer one sort to another?

A variety of reasons will be put forward:
▲ 'I think my Dad likes the colour.'
▲ 'It's good for mopping up the baby's cereal.'
▲ 'We always buy the cheapest.'

Tell the children that they are going to carry out an investigation to see which cloth is best for mopping up. They may be more comfortable using a form of words such as 'Which mopper-upper is best?'.

In more standard English, however, the idea to be tested will be:

Which material is best for mopping up spills?
At this point you will have to decide with the children what makes one cloth (or mopper-upper) better than another. This could be based on cost, value for money, aesthetic values, or its performance as an absorbent material. Decide which of these the children should explore – there is good educational potential in all of them, but this lesson plan assumes that the children will investigate the absorbent qualities of the materials provided. Once this has been established the children will need time to plan their test. Ask them:
▲ How are you going to work out which is the best for mopping up the water?
▲ What will you do?
▲ How much water will you spill?
▲ Who will do the mopping up?
▲ How will you decide if the cloth or paper product has been good at mopping up?

At this point, depending on the age and ability of the children, a note could be made of the procedure which will be followed. If several different ideas arise children should follow their own procedures if at all possible.

When the children start the investigation check that they will be able to remember their results – some may be able to formulate a simple recording table. A blank sheet of paper may be the best option for this as there are a great many different ways of reaching a result and no single recording sheet would service *all* the possible approaches children could adopt.

Question the children to check that their method was consistent and that their results are valid:
▲ Did you use the same amount of water each time?
▲ Who checked to see if the water was mopped up?
▲ Did everyone agree?
▲ Would it be the same if you tried it again?

Be aware that some children may try to prove that the cloth they use at home is the best, even ignoring the evidence before them in order to defend their parents' buying habits!

As the investigation comes to an end, encourage the children to tell the others what they have found out.
▲ Do other groups agree?
▲ What different conclusions have you reached, and why?

Suggestion(s) for extension
If the children have not already come up with a range of different ideas for investigation, you could suggest to a more able group that they repeat the test but use a different method. One possible way is to cut strips of the material and suspend them in a bowl of water, then watch to see how much water is soaked up into the material. Older children will debate the best way of testing a cloth. They may suggest that the variables can be reduced by always having the same person doing the test or by always using the same surfaces. They may like to carry out a survey of favourite mopper-uppers amongst adults in school.

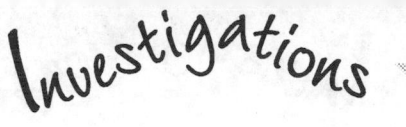

Suggestion(s) for support

With younger and less able children the variables in the actual investigation should be limited. (This does not mean that you need to reduce the range of materials used in the whole lesson.)

Start in the same way as suggested above but before reaching the point at which testing starts, spend some additional time sorting and looking closely at the cloths. You may like to create your collection of materials with this sorting exercise in mind, including different-coloured cloths of the same kind so that the children can sort them first for colour, and then for the properties of the cloth. When testing the materials choose just two to compare and, if the children are able to cope with these two, add one more for comparison.

Assessment opportunities

Watch to see which children are taking the lead with their ideas for the investigation and for those who are able to come up with ways of recording and communicating their findings.

Display ideas

The cloths and paper products can form a colourful display. Surround these with questions about absorbency and examples of the children's findings from the investigation.

Other aspects of the Science PoS covered

Materials and their Properties – 1a, 1e.

◆ ⬡ ELASTICITY

Which material makes the best car launcher?

†† *Whole class split into groups or groups in turn.*

🕐 *50 minutes.*

⚠ *In this lesson children will be using materials to send a toy car across the room as a projectile. Choose the materials used for the car launchers with safety in mind and try each material before the lesson.*

Previous skills/knowledge needed

This investigation builds on the children's knowledge of materials developed in the lesson on page 62.

Preparation

Collect a variety of materials suitable as car launchers (see 'Resources needed'). Select an appropriate wheeled toy (at least one per group) which can be launched as part of the testing procedure. Try out the materials and the toys to check that they work and do not pose a safety hazard. Leave each length of material tied to the chair legs after it has been tested so that it is ready for the children to use. In this investigation children will be involved in a potentially exciting, hands-on experience, so think carefully about the structure of the

groups to make sure that every child has the opportunity to learn and develop their skills.

Resources needed

Large sheets of paper, coloured chalks and/or crayons, standard classroom chairs or stools, wheeled toys/cars, at least two lengths of various types of stretchy and not-so-stretchy material, such as bandage, stockings, socks, towelling, neck ties, strips cut from old sheets and items of clothing. You could include a piece of bicycle inner tube or some wide elastic, but be careful of safety aspects if using these items! All materials should be old or scrap as they will be cut up as part of the recording process. The number of different types of material will depend on the children's ability to cope with the data generated by the testing – five to eight different types should be about right. You will also need set rings if you are going to sort the collection of materials before beginning testing.

What to do

Ask the children if they remember what they have learned about the stretchiness of materials. Encourage them to identify some very stretchy and not-so-stretchy materials. If they need time to revise this information allow them to sort a collection of stretchy and not-so-stretchy materials before going on. Give them set rings to help them with the sorting.

If the children are finding it easy to recall what they have done and learned previously go straight to putting the materials in rank order.

Split the children into groups and give each group one piece of each of the chosen materials. Ask the children:

▲ Which material do you think is the stretchiest?

▲ Which one is the least stretchy?

▲ Can you put the materials in order from the stretchiest to the least stretchy?

Now check to see if all the groups have come up with the same order. If they have not, then so much the better! This will really stimulate discussion.

Each group will need to record their order in some way. If the materials are different colours then these colours can be used as a means of recording, though you will need to guard against the danger of some children thinking that all red things are stretchy.

If there is no easy way to differentiate between the materials then stop at this point to make sure that everyone can clearly identify each one. This can be done in two ways:
▲ Give each sample of material a letter or number.
▲ Ask the children to invent descriptive names for the materials.

If the second method is used then children are challenged to look more closely at the materials, giving them a better chance of relating the performance of the material to its properties. They may offer descriptive names like:
▲ The rough one with the big stitches.
▲ The stripy pyjama one.

When you are sure that the children can identify each sample reliably, and have recorded the order of their materials, continue to the next part of the lesson.

Show the children a chair with a sample of material tied between the chair legs. Show them also how the material can be used to shoot or launch a car along the floor. Some children will find the prospect of trying this very exciting and may need time to play with the cars before they are able to concentrate on designing any testing situation!

When the children are ready, ask them to tell you if they think the rank order of stretchiness created earlier in the lesson will provide the order for the best car launcher. To get their full attention draw them away from the testing area and talk to them as a group or whole class again. Give them time to think about how they would find out:
▲ Which would be the best car launcher?
▲ What would you have to do?
▲ How would this tell you the answer to the question?
▲ Who would do the launching?
▲ Where would the cars finish?
▲ Would you use all the cars or only one?

Check that the children have a workable system for testing the materials and have organised some way of recording their test results. One simple way is to draw a different coloured chalk line for the distance travelled each time.

At the end of the test pupils should be given the opportunity to offer feedback to you and the rest of the class.
▲ Was your prediction correct?
▲ Do you need to alter the order of the materials?

Suggestion(s) for extension
Older and more able children may be able to measure or compare the distance travelled by the cars. This data can be turned into a simple chart.

Suggestion(s) for support
Children who find it difficult to place the samples of materials in rank order will need to:
▲ Sort the collection of materials.
▲ Compare just two samples of material.

Make sure that the younger and less able children are not confused by having samples which are *too* similar and that the wheeled toy used to test the materials is easy to handle.

Assessment opportunities
The sorting and rank ordering part of the lesson will provide an indication of the way in which individual children have retained what they have been taught earlier. This form of assessment can only be carried out if you are actually watching the group, so think about where the groups will be positioned if you wish to focus your assessment on certain individual children. Take particular note of those children who can identify the variables during this investigation. Does anyone suggest that it might make a difference how far back the material is pulled. Are suggestions made to overcome any factors that make the test unfair.

Display ideas
Samples can be cut from each of the pieces of material and stuck in order along a large piece of paper or card. Make one set to show the original prediction, and a second to show the final result. If these are the same pupils can be praised for having good powers of scientific prediction, with a caption such as 'Look what great scientists we are!'. Even if their prediction was inaccurate some positive reinforcement statements can usually be found within the investigative process, such as:
▲ We were good at sorting/measuring.
▲ We looked closely and saw amazing things.
▲ We were clever to find out that ....
▲ Do you like our beautiful pictures/writing about ....?

Other aspects of the Science PoS covered
Physical Processes – 2a, 2b, 2c.
Materials and their Properties – 2a.

Assessment

This chapter contains a series of six lessons which provide opportunities to make summative assessments of what the children in your class know, understand and can do. Ideas for formative assessment are included in each of the lessons in the previous chapters.

The first three lessons provide assessment criteria against which overall attainment in the Life Processes and Living Things, Materials and their Properties and Physical Processes Programmes of Study can be made. The second set of three lessons will allow progressive assessment of the level of scientific skills the children have developed in Experimental and Investigative Science. Each lesson follows a similar pattern to the other lessons in the book.

The method of assessment will include teacher observation, discussion, written, pictorial and graphical work and practical activity. A variety of evidence will be collected to support the assessments.

Use your professional judgement to choose an appropriate time to carry out the assessment lessons. As the assessment objectives are closely linked to the Learning Objectives, which, in turn, are closely linked to the National Curriculum, they could be used at any time to find out the overall attainment of the children, or as end of Key Stage assessments.

PLANTS AND ANIMALS

This activity will assess which pupils:

▲ *are able to recognise and name the external parts of plants;*

▲ *are able to recognise and identify common animals;*

▲ *are able to describe simple features of size, shape and colour of plants and animals;*

▲ *know that plants need water and light to help them grow;*

▲ *know that animals need food and water to survive;*

▲ *know that animals and plants are found in different places;*

▲ *can give reasons how plants and animals are suited to their environment;*

▲ *can sort living things according to observable similarities and differences.*

†† *Task 1: Individual; Task 2: Small group;*
Task 3: Individual or paired; Task 4: Small group.

🕐 *Task 1: 10 minutes; Task 2: 15 minutes;*
Task 3: 15 minutes; Task 4: 15 minutes.

Introduction

This assessment can be achieved by working through four tasks which involve observation, discussion, sorting and playing a matching game of dominoes. It is probably only possible to assess up to six children at a time. You could therefore do the tasks one at a time with a particular group of children or, with an additional helper, you could set up all four tasks to rotate during the day. Not all pupils will need to complete all of the tasks and you should use your professional judgement to decide which tasks are appropriate for each child in your class. You may already know which pupils have achieved the assessment objectives.

Previous skills/knowledge needed

The children should have had the opportunity for lengthy, first-hand study of plants and animals in their natural environment.

Preparation

Take sufficient copies of the photocopiable sheet on page 125.

Make enough plant and animals picture sets from the photocopiable sheet on page 130. You may find it useful to mount the pictures on card and protect them with spray or cling film.

Make copies of the dominoes game on the photocopiable sheet on page 151. You need one copy for each child, or one copy between two.

Resources needed

Task 1: *Either* six flowering plants (spread around the room so that children cannot copy each other's work), six sets of labels for root, leaf, flower and stem; *or* a copy of the photocopiable sheet on page 125 for each child, pencils.

Task 2: Two different flowering plants (you could use any indoor bulb and a chrysanthemum), paper, pencils.

Task 3: One dominoes game for each child or one between two children.

Task 4: A set of plant and animal picture cards, an area for each child to spread out and sort the pictures, set rings.

What to do

Task 1

Either give the children the labels and a plant and ask them to label the root, leaf, stem and flower; *or* give them a copy of the photocopiable sheet on page 125 and explain how they should complete it. The children should have a second activity to do when they have finished in case you are busy with another group. As soon as you have time, go around and check which children have successfully completed the task.

Task 2

Gather a small group of children around two flowering plants. This could be two plants in the classroom or in the school grounds; two different species of tree are also suitable. Keeping the assessment objectives in mind, ask them to tell you something about the plants.

▲ Do the children notice any differences or similarities?

▲ Do they refer to the size, shape and colour of the leaves, flowers and plants?

▲ Do they compare the height and size of the stalks?

▲ Do any of the children tell you something about the plants beyond what they see (such as 'the seed is called an acorn')?

Ask the children to record their observations. Can they write down (or use a scribe to write for them) at least three things about the plants that are the same and at least three things that are different?

Make a note of the children who use their other senses to notice further similarities and differences.

Task 3

Give the children the dominoes from the photocopiable sheet on page 151. Spend five minutes explaining the task, looking at, and discussing, the pictures and sentences. If necessary read the sentences to the children and explain what the pictures are. Ask the children to join the pictures and sentences together in a long line. Show them which card starts and which one finishes the game. An additional helper can observe and make a note of the children who can do this unaided and those who needed help.

Task 4

Gather the children around a small group of tables. Give each child a set of plant and animal picture cards which they should spread out in front of them. Give the children five minutes to look at and talk about the plants and animals in the pictures. Careful observation at this time will allow you to note which children know the simple features of size, shape and colour of plants and animals and the more complex features of the way animals move, where they live and the number of legs they have.

Play a 'Can you find' game. Ask the children to hold up the picture of the snail, ladybird, buttercup, and so on. Can they find an animal or plant that lives in water, or in a wood, or by the seaside? Make a note of those who can. After a few minutes ask the children to sort the pictures, choosing their own criteria. This will vary according to the ability of the child. Children with lots of sorting experience will use subsets and overlapping sets. If they have not already done so, ask the children to:

▲ Sort the pictures into how the animals move. What do the children notice about the animals' features and the way these relate to the animal's movements?

▲ Sort the pictures into where the animals and plants live and grow. What do they notice about the features and their relationship to the plants' and animals' habitats?

To avoid the possibility of copying, give the children different sorting criteria.

How to use the assessment

Use the assessment objectives given on page 102 to make a note of what the children know or do not know, can or cannot do. The worksheets, teacher's observations and notes will provide evidence of achievement for the plants and animals and classification part of 'Life Processes and Living Things' Programme of Study. The most valuable parts of these tasks are the comments the children make during the informal talking and playing.

Reference to photocopiable sheets

The photocopiable sheet on page 125 will provide evidence of the children's ability to recognise and name the external parts of plants.

The photocopiable sheet on page 130 provides pictures of plants and animals. By using these you will discover if the children are able to recognise and identify common animals, know that plants and animals are found in different places, can sort things according to observable similarities and differences and can suggest how plants and animals are suited to their environment. Alternatively, you could use photographs and pictures cut from magazines.

The photocopiable sheet on page 151 can be used to make a simple game of dominoes which will tell you if the children know that plants need water and light to help them grow and that animals and plants need food and water to survive.

SCIENCE

BUTTONS

This activity will assess which pupils are able to:
▲ *sort according to similarities and differences of texture and appearance;*
▲ *sort materials according to the properties of transparency, magnetism, stretchiness, bendiness, shininess, rigidity and squashiness;*
▲ *recognise and name common types of materials;*
▲ *identify which material is best suited to a specific use;*
or
▲ *explore using appropriate senses;*
▲ *make observations;*
▲ *make comparisons and measurements;*
▲ *record results using simple drawings, charts and bar charts;*
▲ *draw conclusions from their results.*
†† *Small-group activity.*
🕐 *Task 1: 10 minutes; Task 2: 10 minutes;*
Task 3: 10 minutes; Task 4: 10 minutes.

Introduction
This activity can be used to assess grouping materials *or* the investigative skills of sorting, observing, comparing, measuring, recording and drawing conclusions; *or* to provide reinforcement for the grouping materials section of 'Materials and their Properties' for those children who require it. The activity is broad enough to allow most children scope to show what they can do. It should also allow you to focus in on your chosen assessment objectives.

Previous skills/knowledge needed
The children should have explored and investigated materials and their properties. They should also have had lots of experience of sorting, comparing, measuring and recording results.

Key background information
Not all children will need to proceed through every task, nor will they all begin at the same starting point. Use your professional judgement to assess which task each child should start from, and after which task she or he should stop.

Preparation
Make a fairly large collection of buttons. Try to include a variety of sizes, shapes and colours; patterned; transparent; made from wood, plastic, metal and rubber; covered in textiles; with different numbers of holes. Your collection could also include sets of identical buttons, toggles and uniform buttons.

Make at least six smaller sets from the larger collection so that you have an example of every variable in each set. Make copies of any photocopiable sheets you plan to use.

Resources needed
All tasks: A collection of buttons, set rings or a large sheet of paper with at least five circles for the children to record their sets.
Task 1: The photocopiable sheet on page 114.
Task 2: The photocopiable sheet on page 152, labels for wood, plastic, metal, fabric, rubber, rock and paper.
Task 3: The photocopiable sheets on pages 115 and 116.
Task 4: The photocopiable sheet on page 153.

What to do
Give each child in the group a selection of buttons which includes all the variables being assessed. Allow them to handle, make comparisons and talk about their collections for about five minutes. Give the children set rings or the large sheets of paper for them to record their sets.

Task 1
Ask the children to sort their collections of buttons into sets. They can choose any criteria they wish. You may find that the more able have already done this during the initial exploratory time.

This task will allow you to assess each child's starting point. Those children who make no attempt to sort should be asked to sort their buttons according to colour, shape, then size, recording their sets on the photocopiable sheet. If you are assessing investigative skills, these children should not proceed any further but should be given more opportunities to sort items according to simple criteria using their senses.

Make a note of those children who successfully sorted their buttons using simple criteria of texture and appearance. Continue to encourage these children to look for other similarities and differences, such as number of holes, pattern, texture and so on. Make a note of any children who suggest sorting the buttons by standard measures, or using comparative criteria.

Task 2
Ask the children to sort the buttons according to the material they are made from. When they have finished, ask them to label their sets. This information can then be transferred to a bar chart using the photocopiable sheet on page 152 if you

wish. The children should then be asked to compare their results with a friend's. Encourage them to ask, or ask yourself, questions like:
▲ Which material was least/most commonly used?
▲ Why were no buttons made of card or rock?

Can the children draw any conclusions from their results?

Task 3

Draw the children's attention to some of the properties of the buttons and ask them to sort their buttons according to these properties. Children who want to put some buttons in two sets should be encouraged to use the photocopiable sheet on page 115. If you are assessing investigation skills, you may wish to assess which children can use and understand Carroll diagrams (the photocopiable sheet on page 116).

Task 4

Give the children copies of the photocopiable sheet on page 153. Read through the questions and explain that they can write or draw their answers. Give the children as much support as they need to complete the sheet without actually giving them any clues to possible answers.

How to use the assessment

Task 1 will allow you to assess which children use their senses to sort objects into sets of similarities and differences. They will also demonstrate whether they are able to sort, measure, compare and record their findings.
Task 2 will show which children can identify and name common materials. The photocopiable sheet on page 152 will provide evidence of which children are able to record results on a simple bar chart, compare results with others and subsequently use the results to draw conclusions.
Task 3 will show which children have a good understanding of the properties of materials, including transparency.
Task 4 will give children the opportunity to

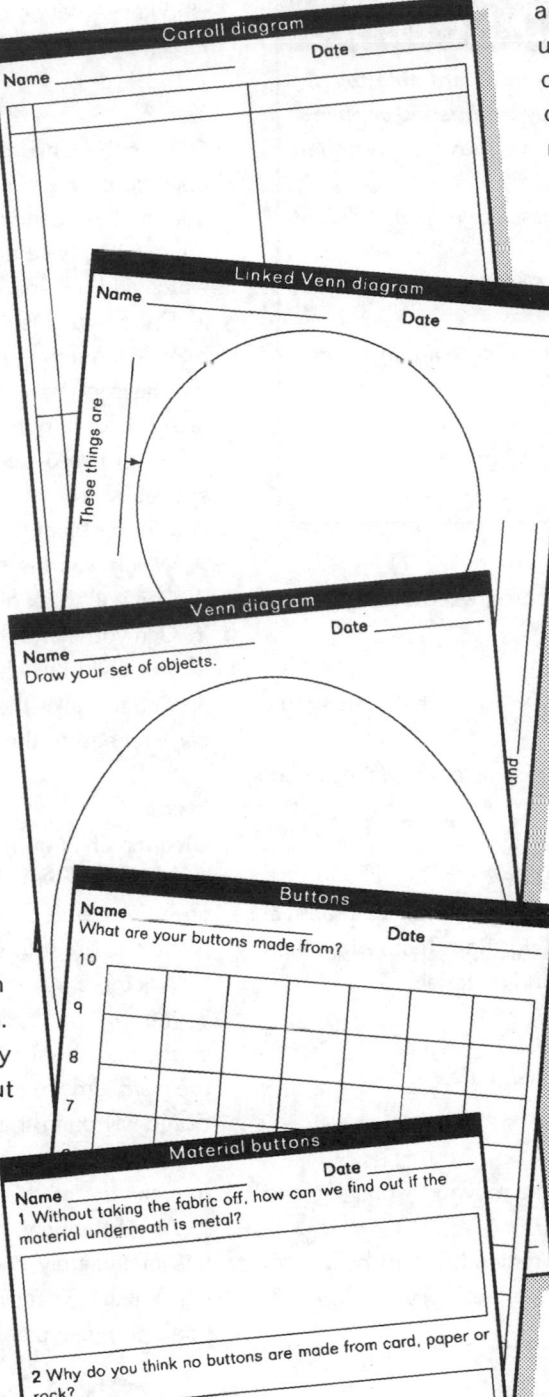

apply their knowledge and understanding of materials to draw conclusions, and demonstrate why they have reached these particular conclusions.

Reference to photocopiable sheets

Buttons are sufficiently small for the children to use the photocopiable sheet on page 114 to display their set. If you have enough buttons, the sorted collection could be glued to a sheet as a permanent record.

The photocopiable sheets on pages 115 and 116 provide examples of overlapping sets and a Carroll diagram for those children who display more sophisticated sorting strategies.

The photocopiable sheet on page 152 is a simple bar chart for the children to record the numbers of wooden, plastic, rubber, fabric, metal, rock and paper buttons they have in their collection.

The photocopiable sheet on page 153 contains questions which check which children know and understand magnetic and non-magnetic materials and how certain materials are suited to specific uses. It may be necessary to read the questions and provide a scribe for those children who have the scientific concepts necessary to answer the questions but lack the reading and writing skills to show what they know, understand and can do. This sheet will provide evidence for the children's level of knowledge and understanding of materials and their properties.

ROCKING AND ROLLING

This activity will assess which pupils are able to:
▲ *show that things move if they are pushed or pulled.*
▲ *compare how some objects move faster than others.*
▲ *compare how some objects move in a different direction.*
▲ *understand that by increasing a force, an object will move faster.*
▲ *understand that by applying a force an object can be made to change direction.*
†† *Small-group activity.*
⏱ *Task 1: 10 minutes; Task 2: 10 minutes; Task 3: 20 minutes.*

Introduction

This activity is made up of a set of progressive tasks so that pupils can:
▲ work through one at a time;
▲ stop when they have obviously reached their conceptual level;
▲ do the one most relevant to your selected assessment objectives.

Previous skills/knowledge needed

The children should have lots of experience of practical activities exploring and investigating the effects of pushes and pulls on a variety of objects and materials.

Preparation

Gather the necessary resources.

Resources needed

Task 1: Wheeled toys which can be moved by pushing and pulling.
Task 2: A board measuring approximately 1m by 50cm, margarine tubs, ping-pong ball, marble, cylindrical pencil, cone, wheeled toy.
Task 3: Marbles, Plasticine, 30cm by 20cm board.

What to do

Task 1

Give each child a wheeled toy and ask if they can make their toys move. Some children will push their toy, while others will pull. Ask the children if they can find another way to make their toy move. Make a note of those who cannot – these children should stop the activity at this point. Those children who know that an object moves if it is pushed or pulled can move on to Task 2.

Task 2

Gather the children around the board and collection of objects. Make a ramp from the board by raising it up with upturned margarine tubs, or similar objects. Explain that you are going to have a race with the objects. Ask the children to watch and tell you what they notice.

Place two objects side by side at the top of the ramp and release them together. Repeat, using two more objects, until you have compared each object with all the others. How many children noticed that some travelled in a straight line, others crooked, some at the same speed, some at different speeds?
▲ Which object went the fastest?
▲ Which was the slowest?
▲ Can you think of a way to make the objects go faster?
▲ Can you make them go slower or change direction?

The children who know that greater or lesser force is applied to make them go faster, slower or change direction can proceed to the next task.

Task 3

Give the children a board, a marble and a ball of Plasticine. Let them play with the marble, rolling it around the board and so on. A game of 'Who can stop the marble rolling off the board?' is great fun.

Ask the children to make the marble roll along the board. Some will push the marble, others will tilt the board. Encourage them to explain what they have done to make the marble move. Ask them to make the marble move faster. Some will push the marble harder, some will tilt the board more. Again encourage them to explain what they have done to make the marble move faster.

Ask if they can make the marble stop. If they do not do this immediately, suggest that they use the Plasticine. Some may roll the Plasticine into a sausage and place it across the board to make a barrier.

Next, ask the children if they can make the marble change direction. The Plasticine can be used to make barriers which, when placed in the correct position, will force the marble to move in a certain direction.

Finally, the children can make a marble run where the marble is placed at the top and runs through a maze of Plasticine barriers before finishing at the bottom. Try putting a target at the bottom for the children to hit.

Ambitious children may wish to use a metal marble which will complete a circuit and light up a bulb or sound a buzzer!

How to use the assessment

Task 1 will assess which children know that things move if they are pushed or pulled. It also offers them the opportunity to describe how their toy moves.

Task 2 allows the children to look at how some objects move faster or slower than others, and some move in a different direction. They can demonstrate how to make things speed up, slow down and stop.

Task 3 allows the children to apply a force to make an object change direction. Some may also notice that the marble changes the shape of the Plasticine if it bumps into it while moving at speed.

ASSESSING AN INVESTIGATION

As children carry out these investigations it should be possible to assess their investigative skills. The following list may be helpful (you will also find this list on the photocopiable sheet on page 156):
▲ observing;
▲ sorting/classifying;
▲ measuring/comparing;
▲ raising questions;
▲ planning/predicting;
▲ testing;
▲ drawing conclusions;
▲ recording;
▲ communicating findings.

Watch the children and listen to them as they carry out an investigation to form a judgement about each child's ability in each skill. It is a complex matter to assess if a child is behaving like a 'real scientist', and for this reason the following assessment lessons rely on the teacher's professional judgement and require a fairly high level of teacher observation. It should, however, prove possible for an individual teacher to gather this useful information as part of everyday classroom work.

Use the following three lessons as they stand or, alternatively, apply the same procedure to other investigative science lessons. A number of lessons in this book could provide good assessment opportunities for investigative science skills, such as:
▲ The 'Buttons' investigation on page 104.
▲ The sorting activities found in many of the lessons in the chapter on Life Processes and Living Things and also the chapter on 'Materials and their Properties'.
▲ The lessons on Experimental and Investigative Science in the 'Investigations' chapter.

LEAVES

This activity will assess the skills of observation, comparing and sorting.

✌ *Small groups or a whole-class lesson with children split into groups.*

🕒 *40 minutes.*

Previous skills/knowledge needed

None required, but if you want to trace the development of these skills over a period of time this exercise can be set as a regular assessment task.

Preparation

First decide who you wish to assess, and why. It may not be necessary to gather evidence of these skills from every child. Some may already have provided sufficient evidence for you to make a judgement. Identify those children on whom you will focus your attention, as this may have implications for pupil grouping and seating arrangements within the classroom.

Make a collection of objects which have a wide range of variables. Natural objects are particularly good for this, so the following example uses leaves.

Resources needed

Sheets of good drawing paper, soft drawing pencils, a collection of leaves. These should be from more than one species of tree (two different species would be sufficient but you can include more if you wish).
As a minimum, you should collect enough leaves for each child being assessed to have one of each kind.

What to do

Give every child one leaf and ask them to look at it closely, noticing all the tiny details. Encourage the children to draw what they see while talking to those children on whom you

have chosen to focus.

Ask the children to show you what they have noticed, and make a note of the detail each has observed. Make notes or use the photocopiable sheet on page 156 to make a record.

When each child has been questioned offer those who would benefit from it the chance to use hand magnifiers or perhaps microscopes.

The assessment activity could be stopped at this point, but it is usually possible to go on to the next stage assessing the children's ability to make comparisons.

Give out the leaf samples from a second tree species, one per child. Ask pupils to compare the two leaves, finding some things which are the same and some things which are different about them. Draw ideas from your focus children or, if they are able, ask them to write some of the similarities and differences down. Make a note of significant factors, such as a child who is unable to give you any similarities, or an individual who goes beyond the simple criteria of size, shape and colour when comparing the leaves.

Finally, assess the children's ability to sort. Give each group a large selection of leaves and ask them to sort these. Use this sorting time to check any individuals who have shown evidence of having particularly well-developed or poorly-developed skills. Ask them to sort a small collection while you watch and question them about the criteria they are using for sorting.

▲ Has the child done, or said, anything particularly noteworthy?

▲ Are there causes for concern or any exceptional factors to note?

▲ How does the assessment assist in planning future activities with this child?

To finish the lesson you can ask those children who you judge to have the ability to make a list of all the different ways the leaves could be sorted.

Reference to photocopiable sheet

The photocopiable sheet on page 156 can be adapted to suit your school or individual recording system. If you do not have a system for recording the development of scientific skills you could use the National Curriculum levels as a guide and insert a number 1, 2 or 3 to correspond with a level description. However, the level descriptions have not been written for this purpose and you may prefer to create your own scale.

Skills recording sheet:
Child's name
observing
sorting/classifying
measuring/comparing
raising questions
planning/predicting
testing
drawing conclusions
recording
communicating findings

MEASURING BALLS

This activity will assess the skills of comparing, measuring and raising questions.

†† *Individual assessment activity which could lead to a group discussion.*

🕑 *40 minutes.*

Previous skills/knowledge needed

The skills assessed in this lesson are fairly demanding, so it is unlikely that you will be able to carry out the activity unless the children have already had opportunities to practise the skills of comparing, measuring and raising questions.

Preparation

Make a collection of different balls from the PE store and other sources. Include as many different types, sizes and shapes of ball as possible, such as a rugby ball, power bouncing ball, golf ball, airflow ball or one of each type held in your regular school stock.

Decide on the pupils you are going to assess and why. For most children individual assessment will not be necessary as they will yield sufficient evidence of their abilities during the course of other science lessons.

Resources needed

A collection of balls, measuring instruments (rulers of different lengths, tape-measures, large callipers, capacity measures, pan balances), large sheets of paper, large felt-tipped pens or crayons.

If you are going to attempt the assessment while in charge of the whole class you will need some additional adult support.

What to do

Talk to the individual being assessed about the collection of balls and ask her to put the balls into rank order.

Check to see what criterion has been used for the ordering. Most children will rank order according to size, so ask if they can think of any other way, perhaps weight or volume.

Make a note of whether or not the balls have been correctly ranked. If they have, encourage the child to mention any possible alternatives she may have noticed.

Now ask the pupil what she thinks could be measured about the balls. The answer to this question will be closely related to her ability to find alternative ways of ranking the collection. Some children will suggest measuring circumference (although they may not use this word) or some other way of measuring the size of the balls. Others may suggest measuring some other attribute of the balls such as how high the ball will bounce, how long a child can keep the ball in the air, or how far each one can be kicked.

The concept of 'measurement' will vary according to the age and ability of the pupil. You may be happy to accept a straight comparison as a representation of measurement from some children, while insisting on some form of measurement using standard measures from others.

Give the children as much opportunity as possible to demonstrate their ability to measure. If they start by drawing around the balls, encourage them to measure the resulting circles. Ask them if they think it would be possible to measure the balls using different methods. There are many possible answers, with varying levels of sophistication. Individuals may:
▲ use string or a tape-measure to measure circumference;
▲ use a ruler or callipers to measure diameter;
▲ weigh the balls;
▲ immerse the balls in water, then measure the volume of water which is displaced.

It is unlikely that children at Key Stage 1 will be able to carry out the final method suggested above, but it is possible that they may come up with it as an idea. If they do you should note this, along with any other methods for measuring they suggest.

Now give the child the chance to show how well she can actually measure and record, using one or more of her suggested methods. The photocopiable sheet on page 156 could be helpful as a means of summarising what you have observed.

To round off the lesson, ask the child to suggest ideas which can be tested, asking questions, such as:
▲ What do you think we could do with the balls which would help us compare them?

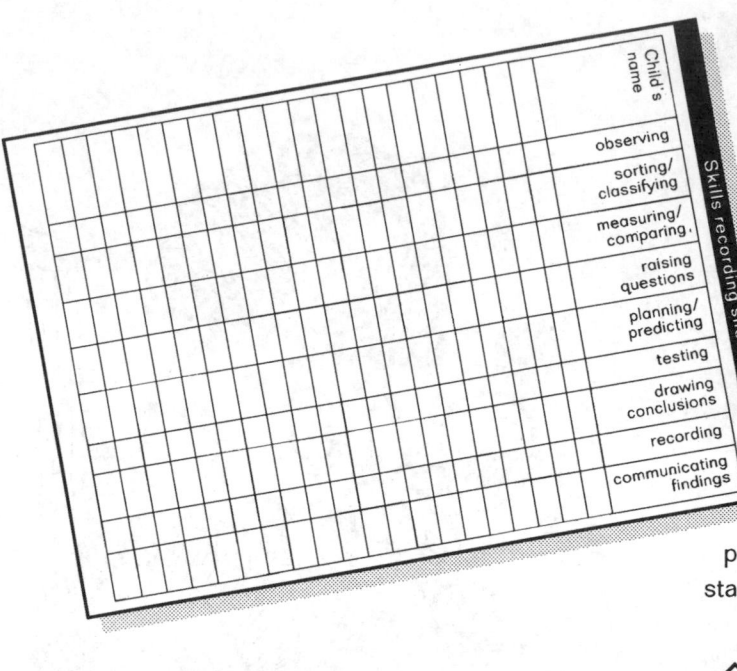

Child's name	observing	sorting/classifying	measuring/comparing,	raising questions	planning/predicting	testing	drawing conclusions	recording	communicating findings

Skills recording sheet

Children may also suggest ideas like:
▲ Which one is best on grass?
▲ How long will each one stay in the air if I kick it hard?
▲ Which is best for playing with on the carpet?
Make a note of their suggestions.

The lesson can finish here, but consider using the children's suggestions as starting points for investigations in subsequent lessons.

Reference to photocopiable sheet

You may wish to note whether the child being assessed is operating within or outside the normal range for her age in the responses she makes. The photocopiable sheet on page 156 is included so that you may record this in the light of your professional judgement and experience. The end of key stage descriptions may also be of help in this respect.

Some children will not be able to come up with any suggestions. Only the most able Key Stage 1 children will be able to generate an idea in this way, so the response to this question is very significant in assessment terms.

If no immediate response is forthcoming, try phrasing the question in a different way:
▲ What question could we ask about these balls?
▲ What could we find out about all these balls?
▲ What sort of things could we test using these balls?
A similar range of responses as before is possible:
▲ How far will they go?
▲ How long will they bounce?

BOUNCING BALLS

This activity will assess the skills of testing, drawing conclusions, recording and communicating outcomes.
†† *Small groups.*
🕐 *45 minutes.*

Previous skills/knowledge needed

The children undertaking this assessment activity will need to have had practical experience of carrying out investigations on a number of occasions.

Preparation

Make a small collection of different kinds of ball from the PE store so that each group of children being assessed has a set. Cut strips of coloured sugar paper so that each group has five different coloured strips of an even width (about 15cm is ideal). Make adequate copies of the photocopiable sheet on page 154 and the optional recording sheet on page 155.

You will need to decide who you want to assess during this lesson and place them in appropriate groups. It may be best to focus on a small number of children gathered together in one group, but if this group would include a particularly forceful child who would take over the activity it may be advisable to create two groups and rotate between these as the lesson progresses.

As with all forms of practical assessment your own judgement, based on what you have seen the children do and heard them say, is of vital importance. For this reason try to organise some additional adult support so that the activity yields the evidence you are seeking.

In the section of the lesson which tests the children's ability to record what they have done, several different forms of recording could be assessed. Choose, in advance of the

lesson, which form of recording you wish to assess (writing, drawing a chart, drawing an annotated diagram or a picture with labels). This may have implications for the types of paper you make available.

Resources needed

A collection of balls, a selection of coloured sugar paper strips, Blu-Tack or similar adhesive suitable for sticking strips to a wall, a metre stick, paper, pencils, copies of the photocopiable sheets on pages 154 and 155.

What to do

Show the children the photocopiable sheet on page 154. This shows how a group of children carried out an investigation into the bounciness of balls. Turn the sheet into a story, if you wish, by telling pupils that these children wanted to find the bounciest ball so that their group would be best at playing a game in a competition.

Help the children to understand what the investigation involved. Ask them:
▲ How did these children find out which ball was bounciest?
▲ How do you think they checked they were right?
▲ Do you think they wrote their results down?
▲ How did they make the test as fair as possible?

At this point take one of the balls from the collection and demonstrate different ways in which the balls could have been dropped in the test procedure, possibly thrown down at the floor, or dropped from a steady hand.
▲ Why would the children have chosen one way of dropping the ball?
▲ How would the children tell which ball bounced highest?
▲ Would it matter where you looked from to tell which was bouncing the highest?

Now tell the children that they are going to carry out the same investigation. Show them the collection of balls and the strips of coloured paper.

Either ask each child to draw a plan of what he is going to do, or allow him to set up the test. Whichever method you choose, this offers an opportunity to carry out individual assessments on the selected pupils. Ask each individual questions to give him an opportunity to show what he understands about setting up a test.
▲ Why are you putting the coloured strips there?
▲ What are you going to do?
▲ How will the test work?
▲ Will that be a good way of doing it?
▲ Will you do it all at once?
▲ Will it make a difference who does what?
▲ How will you be able to tell me what you found out?

Before pupils start to carry out the test hand out the prepared recording sheet or ensure that paper and pencils are at hand.

As the children carry out the investigation take each child aside and check that he can explain what is going on. Also give him a chance to say how he would have done it differently if he had been doing it without everyone else helping and hindering. Check particularly to see if the child recognises the importance of using the same procedure every time and trying things more than once.

Encourage each child to make a record of the results as they happen and to explain what they think the results mean.

When the children have had sufficient time to test the balls you can ask them to sit separately and find a way of explaining what they have found out by writing, drawing a chart or drawing an annotated diagram or picture with labels. What you ask them to do will depend on their previous

Sometimes, those who are not satisfied with the method of testing which was adopted by the group will put forward an alternative strategy at this stage. This should be noted too as it shows an ability to be critical of methodology which is not commonly present at Key Stage 1. Try also to identify those children who have creative ideas for communicating the results of their investigations to others.

Ask the children how they would explain what they have found out to another group who were going to undertake the same investigation.

▲ What would you tell the group to do?

▲ What would you tell the group not to do?

▲ How would you organise things so that the results of the new groups could be compared with your own results?

▲ How would you communicate what you have found out to a big group, like the whole school?

Make a note of the children's ideas and, if you wish, allow them to try some out.

The photocopiable sheet on page 156 could be used to record a summary of the assessment.

Reference to photocopiable sheets

The photocopiable sheet on page 154 is a cartoon story of children investigating bouncy balls. This can be used as a starting point for the lesson. The photocopiable sheet on page 155 provides a table for recording the results of the investigation, while page 156 is an investigation assessment recording summary sheet.

experience and the form of recording you wish to assess.

If the act of independent recording would be beyond the children's capabilities ask them to explain orally what they have found out. Ensure that the forum for giving this explanation allows each child who you want to assess the chance to reveal his understanding. It may be easier to talk to each child individually, in pairs or small groups.

Ask each child to explain what he did and how what he did helped him to find out which ball is the bounciest.

Photocopiables

The pages in this section can be photocopied for use in the classroom or school which has purchased this book, and do not need to be declared in any return in respect of any photocopying licence.

They comprise a varied selection of both pupil and teacher resources, including pupil worksheets, resource material and record sheets to be completed by the teacher or children. The photocopiable sheets are related to one, or more, of the activities in the book; the name of the first relevant activity is indicated at the top of the sheet, together with a page reference indicating where the lesson plan for that activity can be found.

Individual pages are discussed in detail within each lesson plan, accompanied by ideas for adaptation where appropriate – of course, each sheet can be adapted to suit your own needs and those of your class. Sheets can also be coloured, laminated, mounted on to card, enlarged and so on where appropriate.

Pupil worksheets and record sheets have spaces provided for children's names and for noting the date on which each sheet was used. This means that, if so required, they can be included easily within any pupil assessment portfolio.

Feeling surfaces, page 14

Venn diagram

Name _____   **Date** _____

Draw your set of objects.

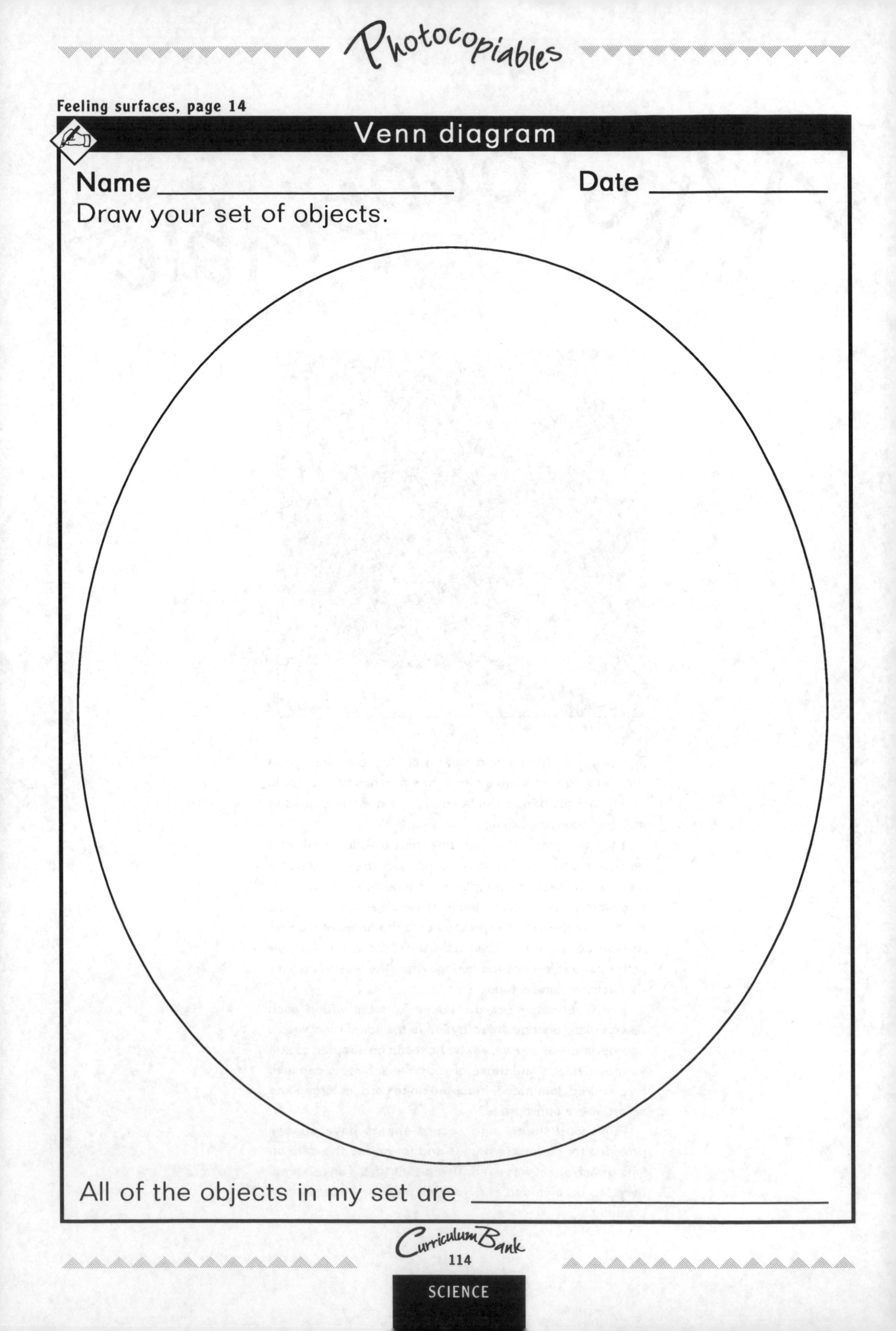

All of the objects in my set are _____

Feeling surfaces, page 14

Linked Venn diagram

Name _____   Date _____

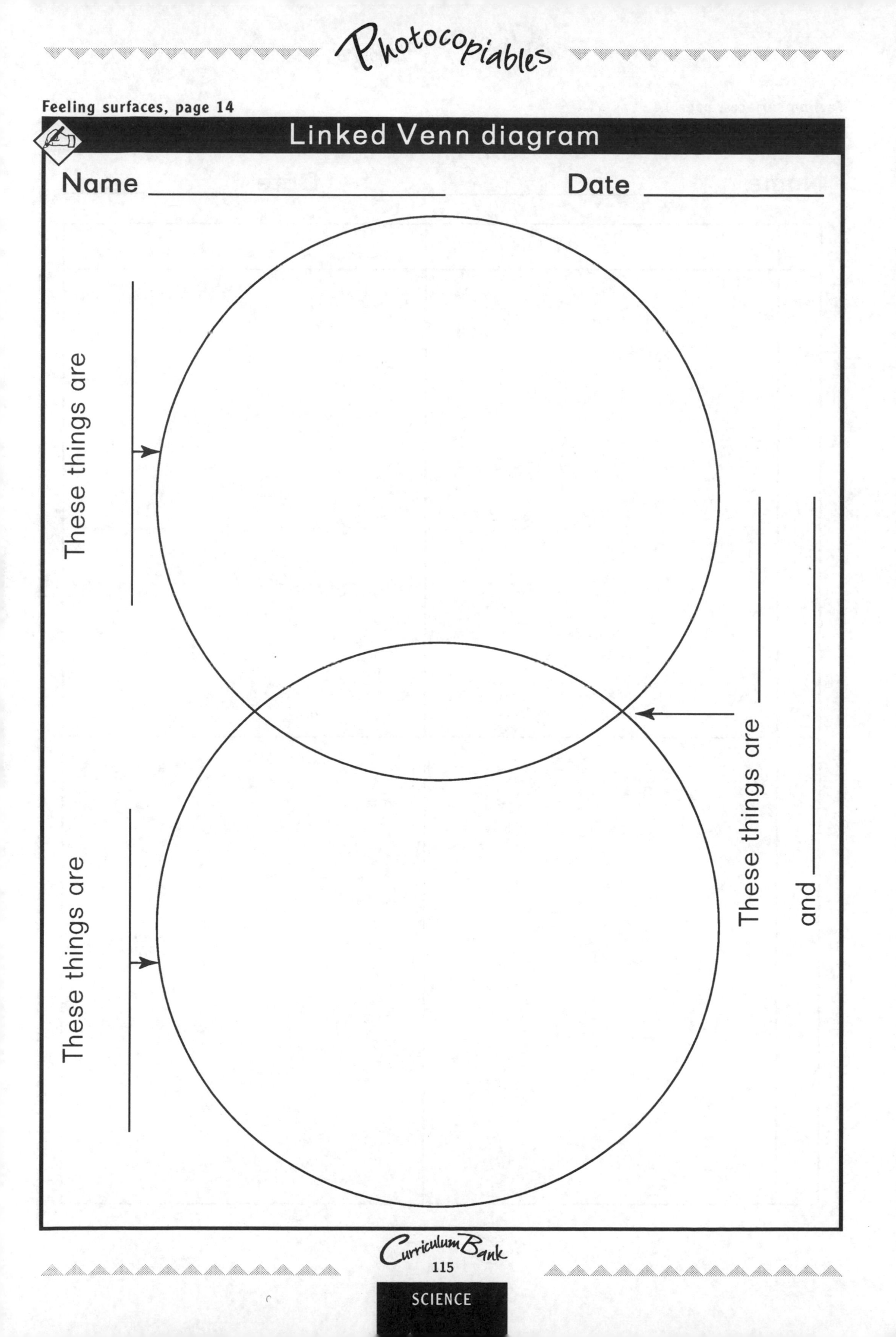

These things are _____

These things are _____

These things are _____

and _____

Feeling surfaces, page 14

Carroll diagram

Name _____   Date _____

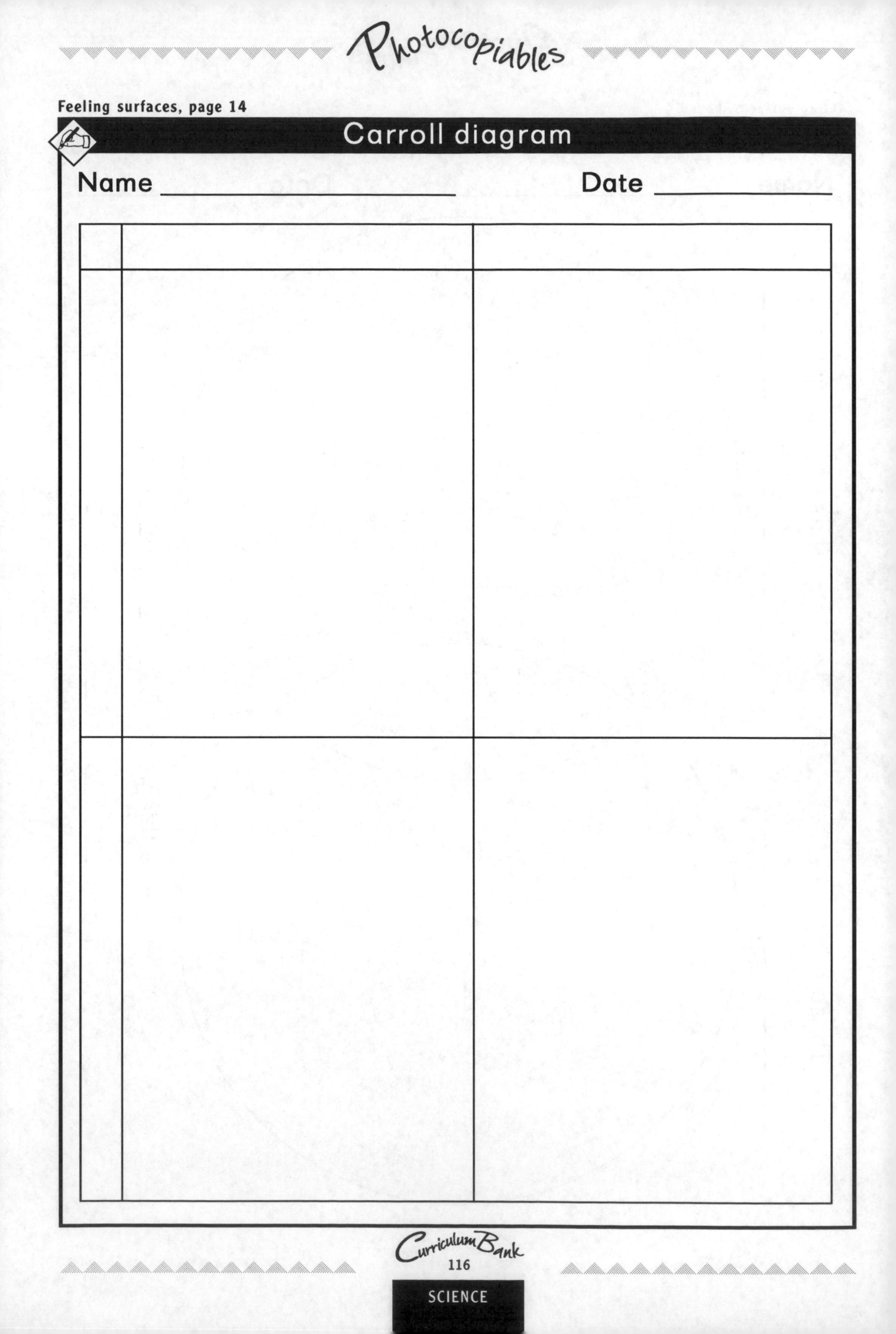

Smelling pots, page 20

Smelling pots

Name _____   **Date** _____

Draw what you think you could smell in each pot.

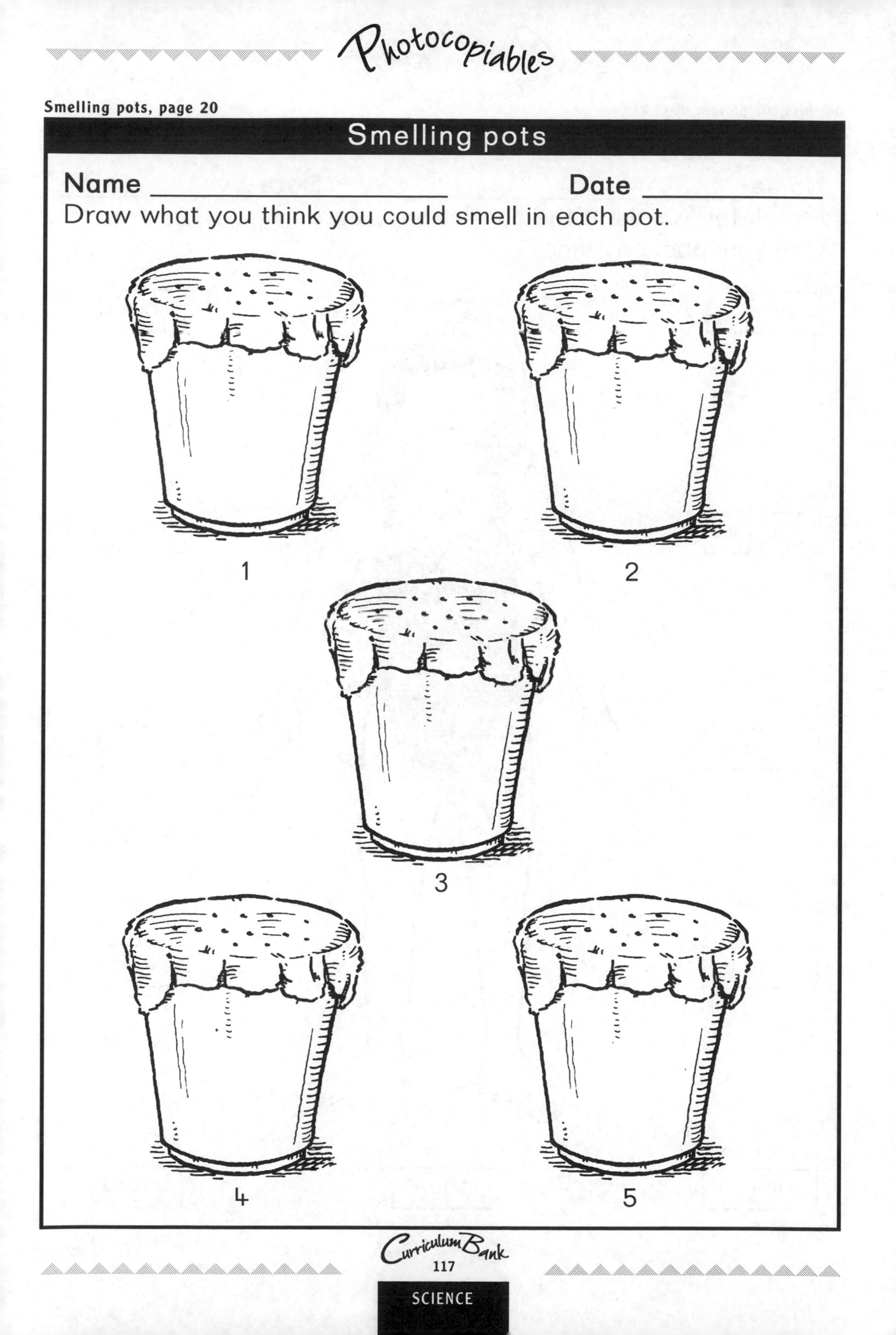

1

2

3

4

5

Body parts

Name _____   **Date** _____

Match the words to the correct body part.
Can you label any more?

body

head

elbow

arm

fingers

hand

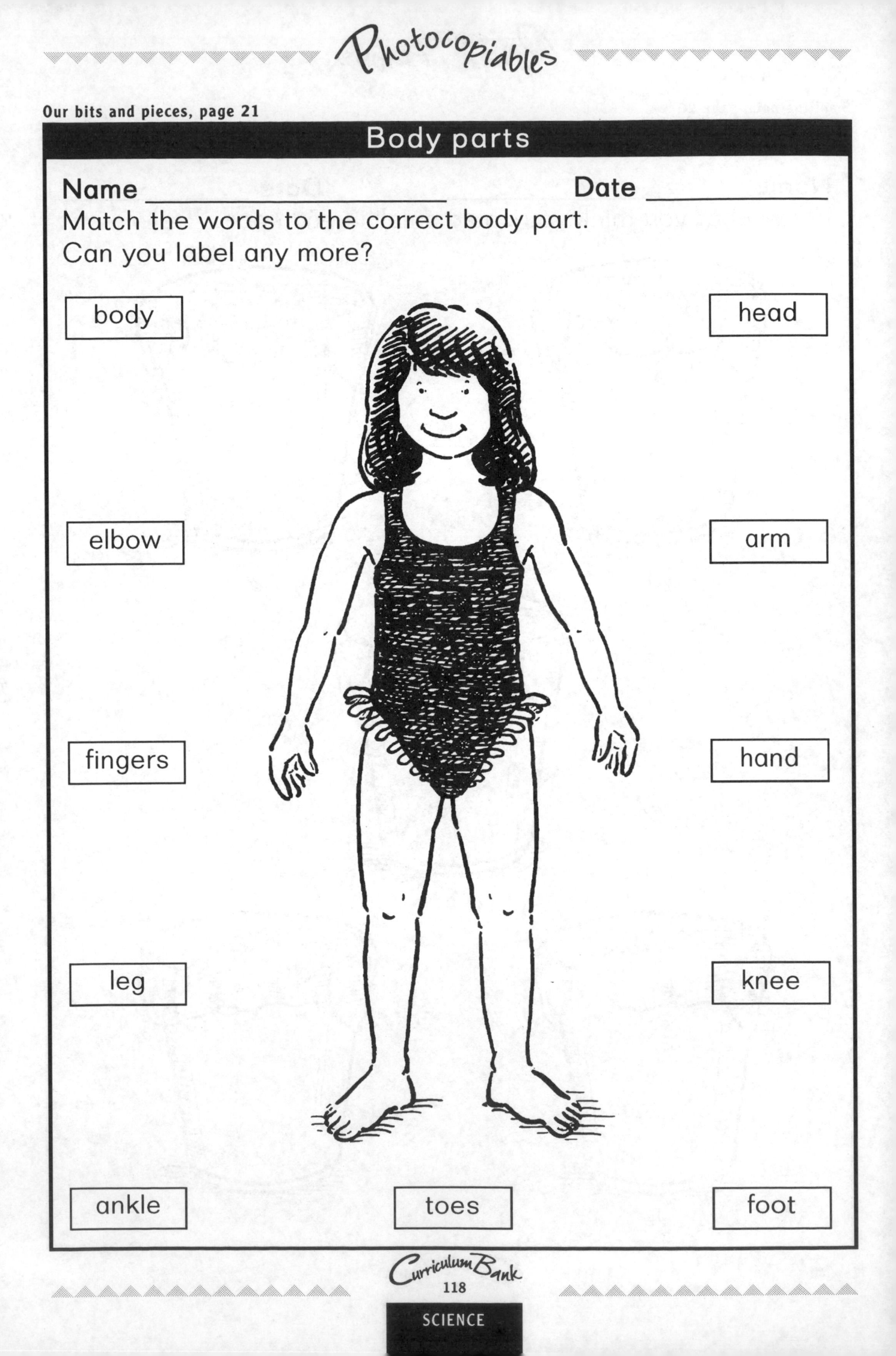

leg

knee

ankle

toes

foot

Our bits and pieces, page 21

Features

Name _____   **Date** _____

Match the word to the correct feature.

| forehead | eyes | nose | chin |

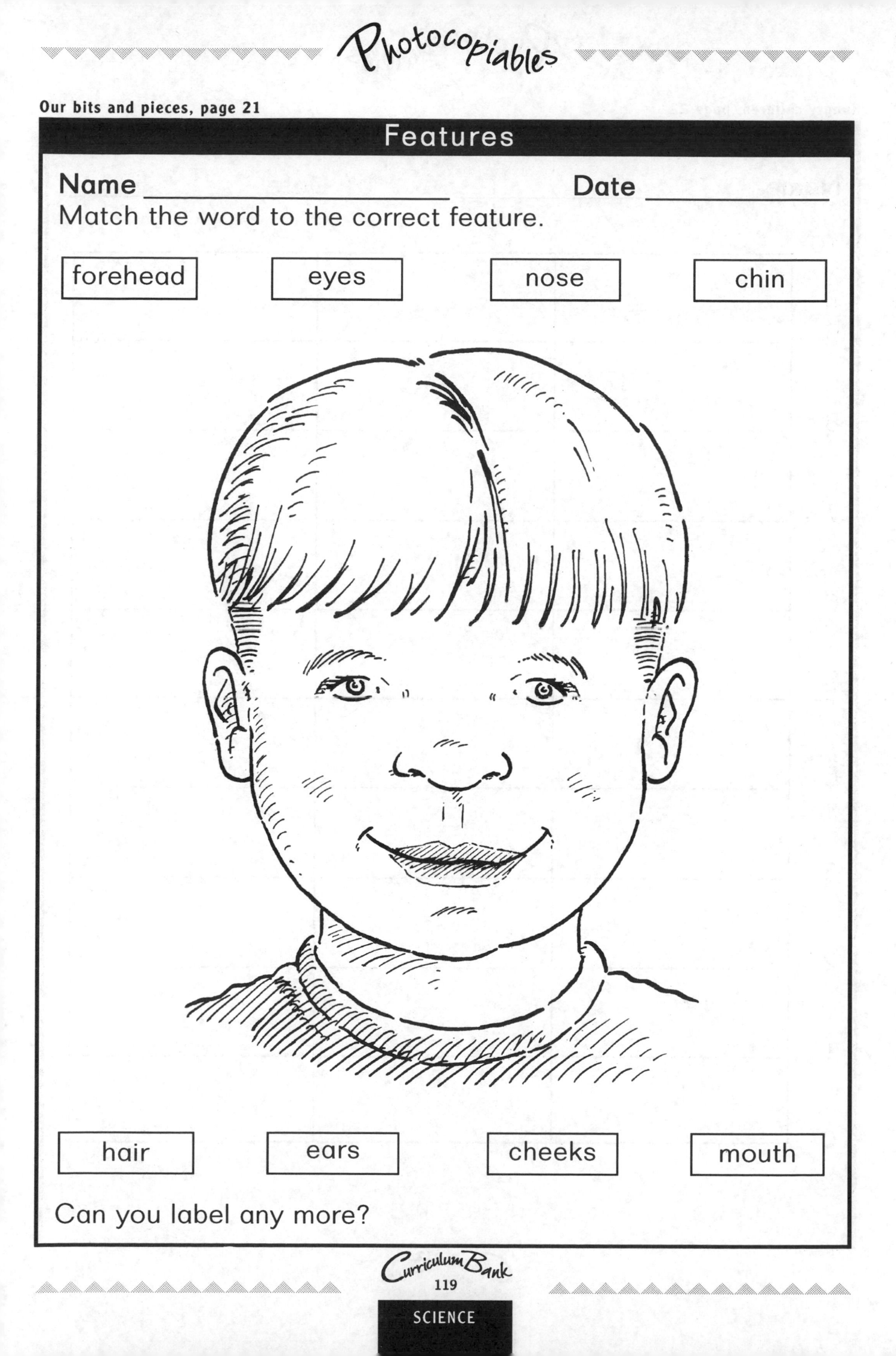

| hair | ears | cheeks | mouth |

Can you label any more?

Hungry children, page 22

Block graph

Name _____ Date _____

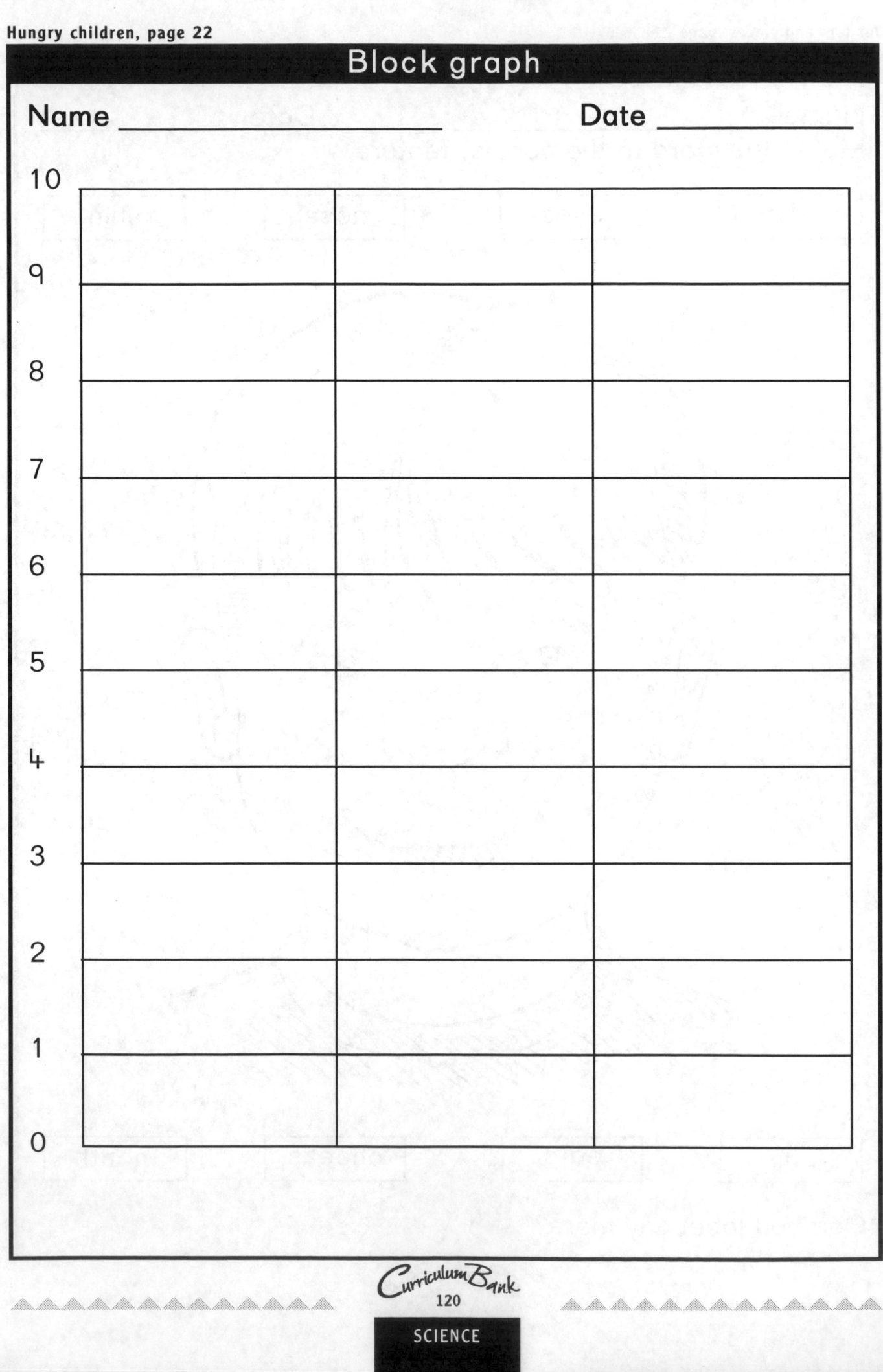

Healthy eating

Name _____ **Date** _____

Draw pictures of some foods which are healthy and some which are not healthy.

healthy (✔)	not healthy (✗)

Medicine and drugs

Name _____   Date _____

Yes (✔) or No (✘)?

Are these things safe to swallow?

Babies

Name _____   **Date** _____

Cut out the pictures and put them in the correct order.

What colour eyes? page 30

Tick or tally chart

Name _____   **Date** _____

Tally (‖‖‖) or tick (✔).

Can you put the information on to a bar chart or block graph?
What does your graph tell you?

Labelling a plant

Name _____   **Date** _____

Write the correct word in each box.

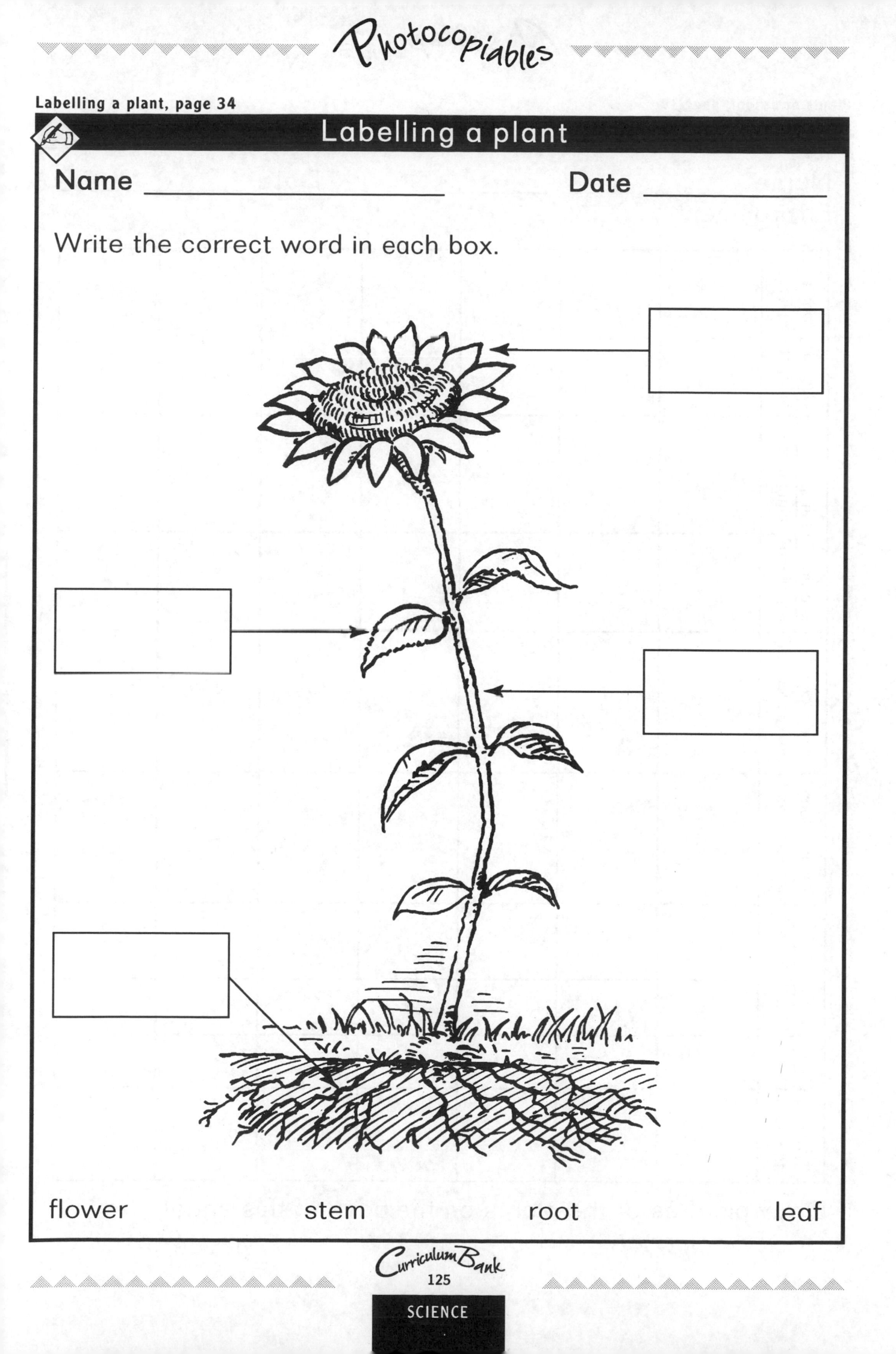

flower   stem   root   leaf

Plants at school, page 39

Plant survey

Name _____   Date _____

Environment:

Name of the plant	Is it a: tree? bush? flower?			What colour is the flower?	What colour are the leaves?	Is it growing in a: dry place? damp place?		Was it growing with other plants?

Draw pictures of the plants on the back of this sheet.

Animals at school, page 39

Animal survey

Name _____   Date _____

Environment:

Name of the animal	Does it:		Does it have:			How many legs does it have?	Did you find it on its own?						
fly?	swim? walk?	a shell?	wings?	feathers?									

Draw pictures of the animals on the back of this sheet.

Plants and animals around us, page 41

Life under and around a stone

Name _____   Date _____

Plants and animals around us, page 41

Life around a pond

Name _____   Date _____

Plants and animals around us, page 41

Plants and animals

Name _____   Date _____

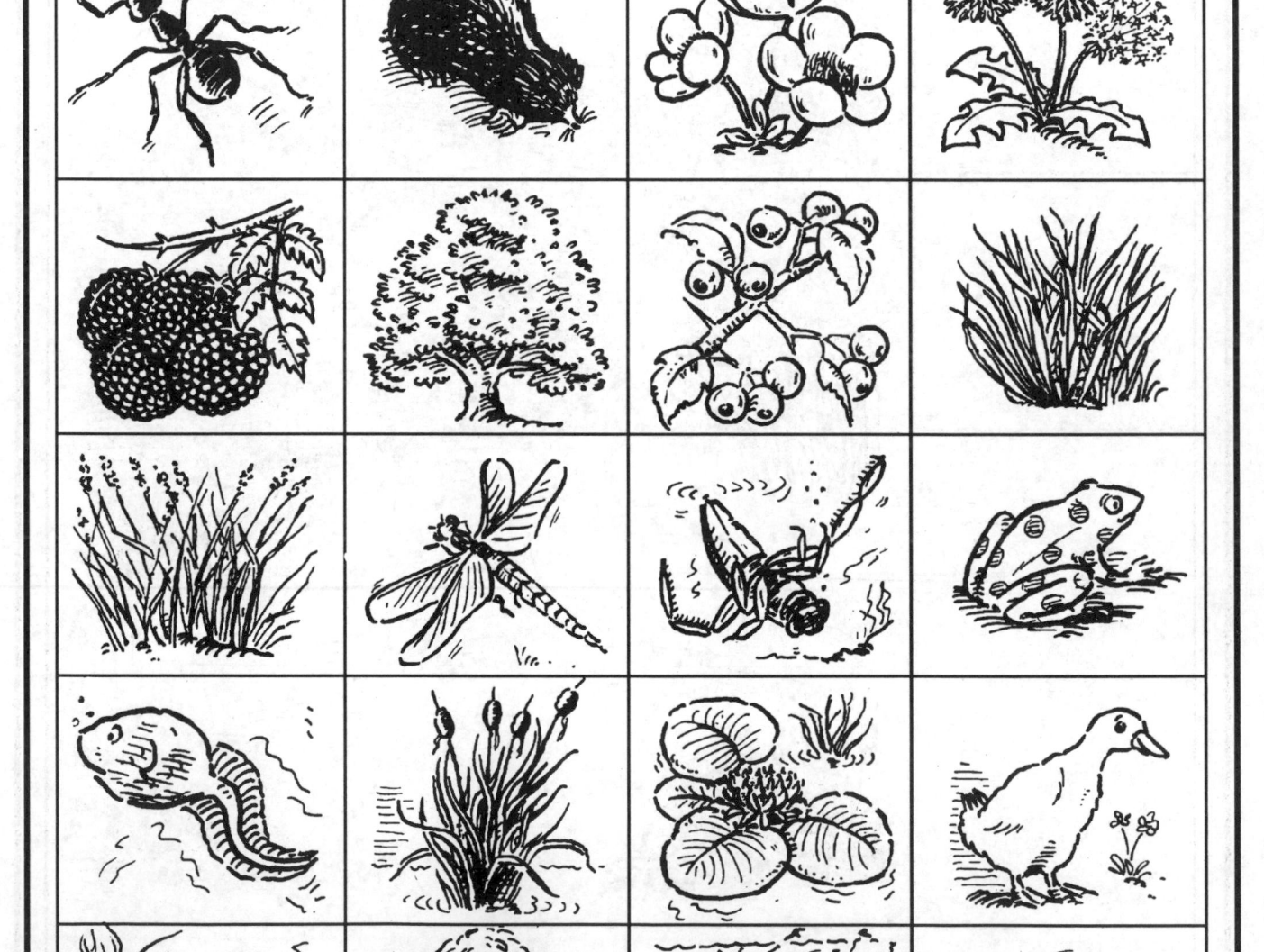

Alive or not? page 44

Living or not

Name _____   Date _____

Knock --- on wood

Name _____   **Date** _____

Draw the pictures.

rough	shiny	dull

smooth	hard	soft

What is the material?

Knock --- on wood

Name _____   Date _____

metal	wood	plastic

rock	paper	textiles

Materials with many uses

Name _____   Date _____

metal	wood	plastic	glass	paper	textiles

Materials with special uses, page 55

Materials with special uses

Name ____________________ Date ____________

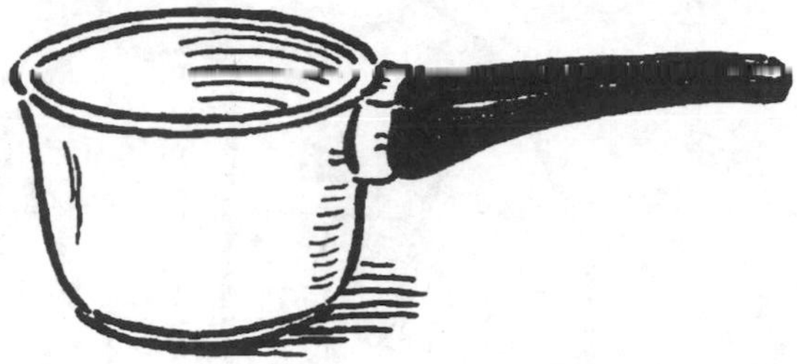

is made of plastic because

____

____

____

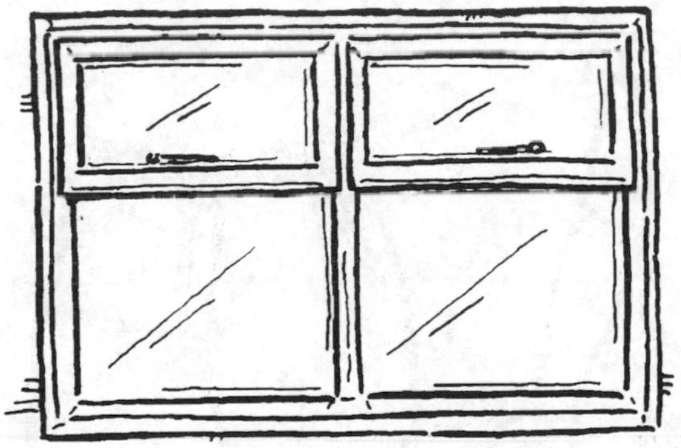

is made of glass because

____

____

____

is made of metal because

____

____

____

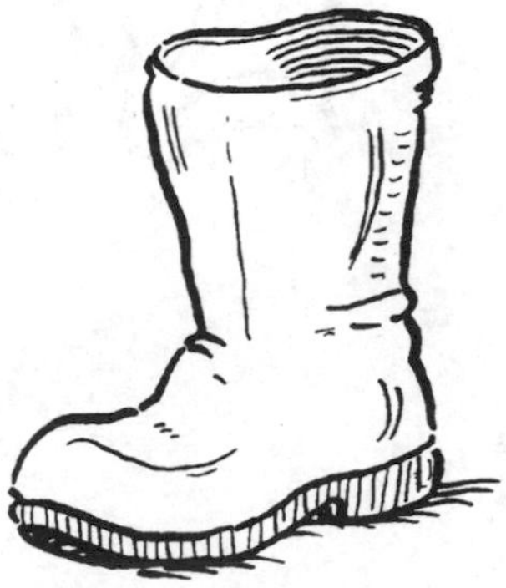

is made of wood or plastic because

____

____

____

Finish the sentences and match them to the correct picture.

Materials with special uses, page 55

Materials with special uses

Name _____ Date _____

Cut out the clothes and dress Sam.

How many more items of clothing do we wear when the weather is cold?

Squashed banana sandwiches, page 57

Bread recipe

500g plain flour
30g margarine
2 level teaspoons of salt
30g fresh yeast
1 level teaspoon of
sugar
500ml milk and water
1 egg

Sieve the salt and flour into a warmed bowl.
Rub the margarine into the flour.

Cream together the sugar and yeast (if using dried yeast following instructions on the packet) and pour this into a well in the centre of the flour.
Add the milk and water a little at a time, mixing all together until the dough leaves the side of the bowl easily.
Turn on to a floured board or table top and knead well.
Put into a clean warm bowl, cover, and leave in a warm place until the dough has doubled in size (about 45 minutes).
Turn on to a floured board or table top and reknead, then form the dough into rolls, or plaited loaves, or press into a loaf tin.
Place on greased and floured baking trays.
Leave in a warm place for 10 minutes, then brush with beaten egg.
Bake at 220°C or Gas Mark 7 for 10–15 minutes for rolls, 20–25 minutes for plaited loaves or 45–50 minutes for a large loaf.

Squashed banana sandwiches, page 57

Making bread

Name _____   Date _____

Cut out the pictures and put them in the right order.

Melting chocolate, page 65

Chewy chocolate cake recipe

75g broken plain chocolate
100g butter
2 eggs
225g sugar
1 teaspoon of vanilla essence
100g plain flour

Line a 20cm square box with plastic cling film.
Put chocolate and butter in a see-through bowl and microwave on high for 1½–2 minutes.
Put the eggs, sugar and vanilla essence into another bowl and beat together until thick and creamy.

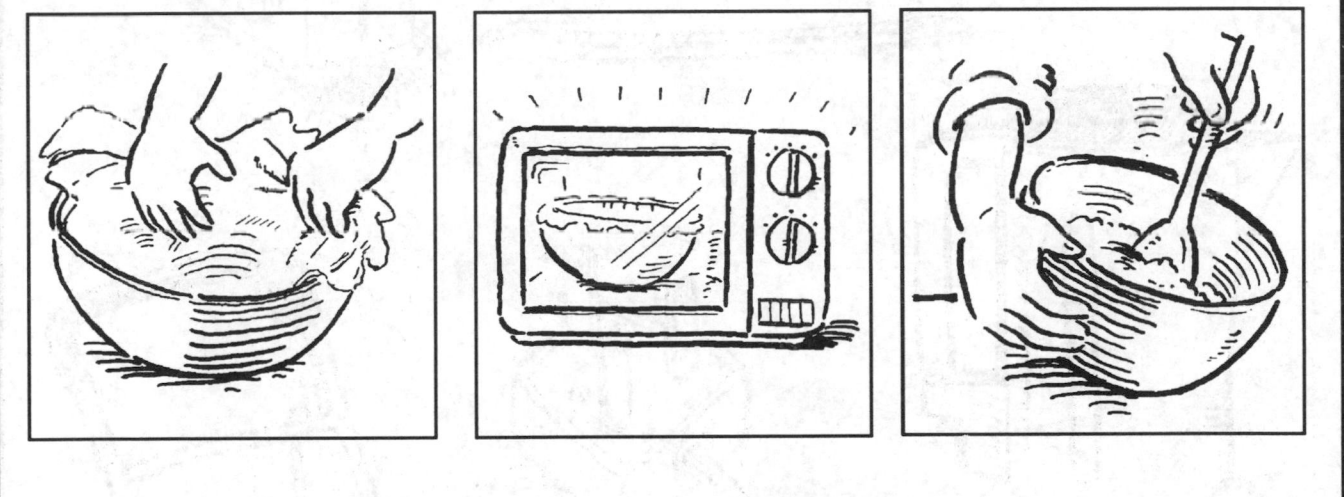

Mix in the flour, and the chocolate mixture, adding one tablespoon of each at a time. Spoon the mixture into the square box and smooth the top. Microwave on high for 5 or 6 minutes, turning the dish every minute if the microwave does not have a turntable.
(The cake can also be cooked in a conventional oven at 180°C, Gas Mark 5 for 30–40 minutes.)

Safe or unsafe?

Name _____   **Date** _____

Put a cross (✗) through the things you should never touch.

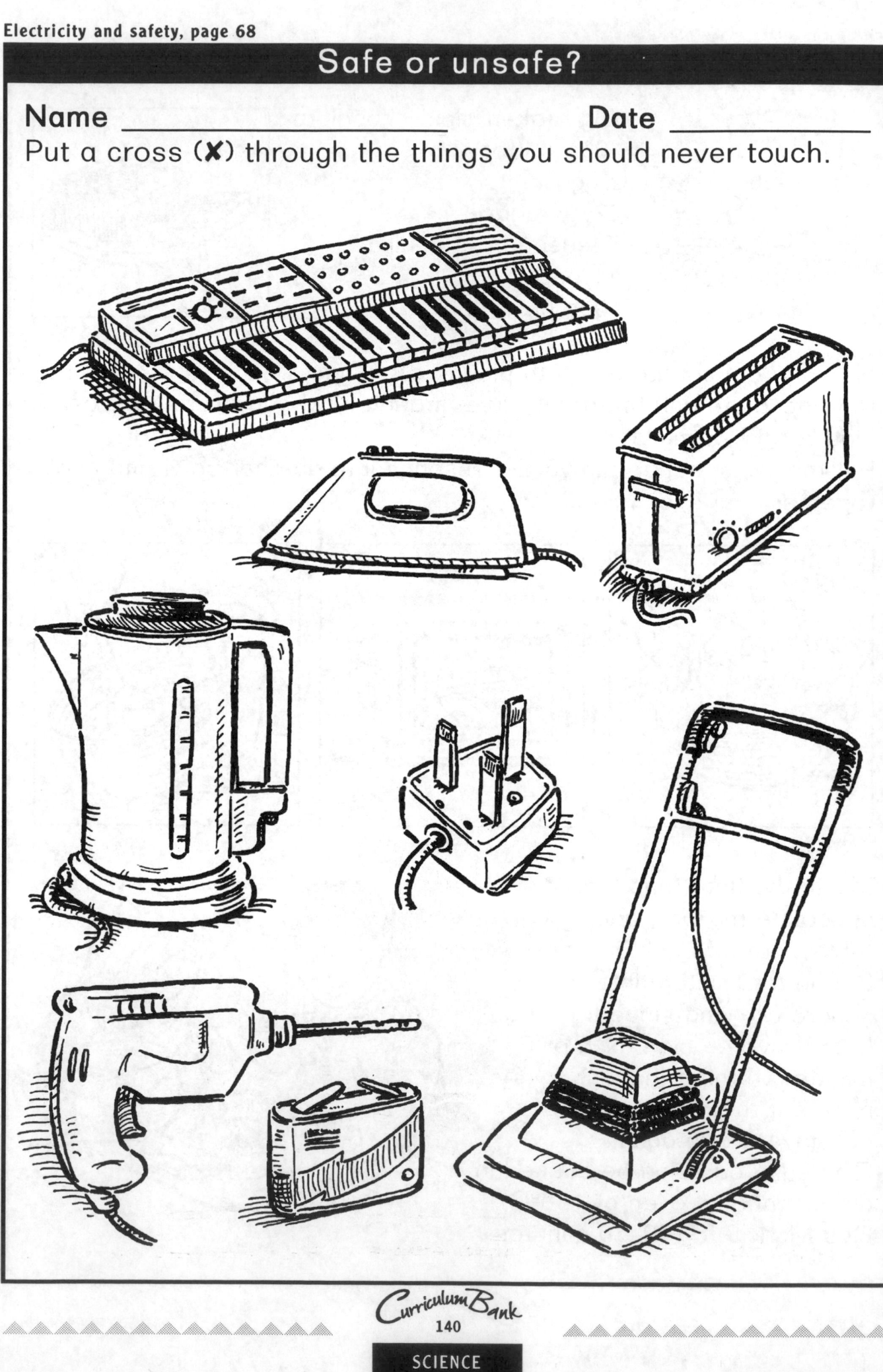

Electricity and safety, page 68

Warning signs

Name _____   **Date** _____

Colour the triangles (△) red.

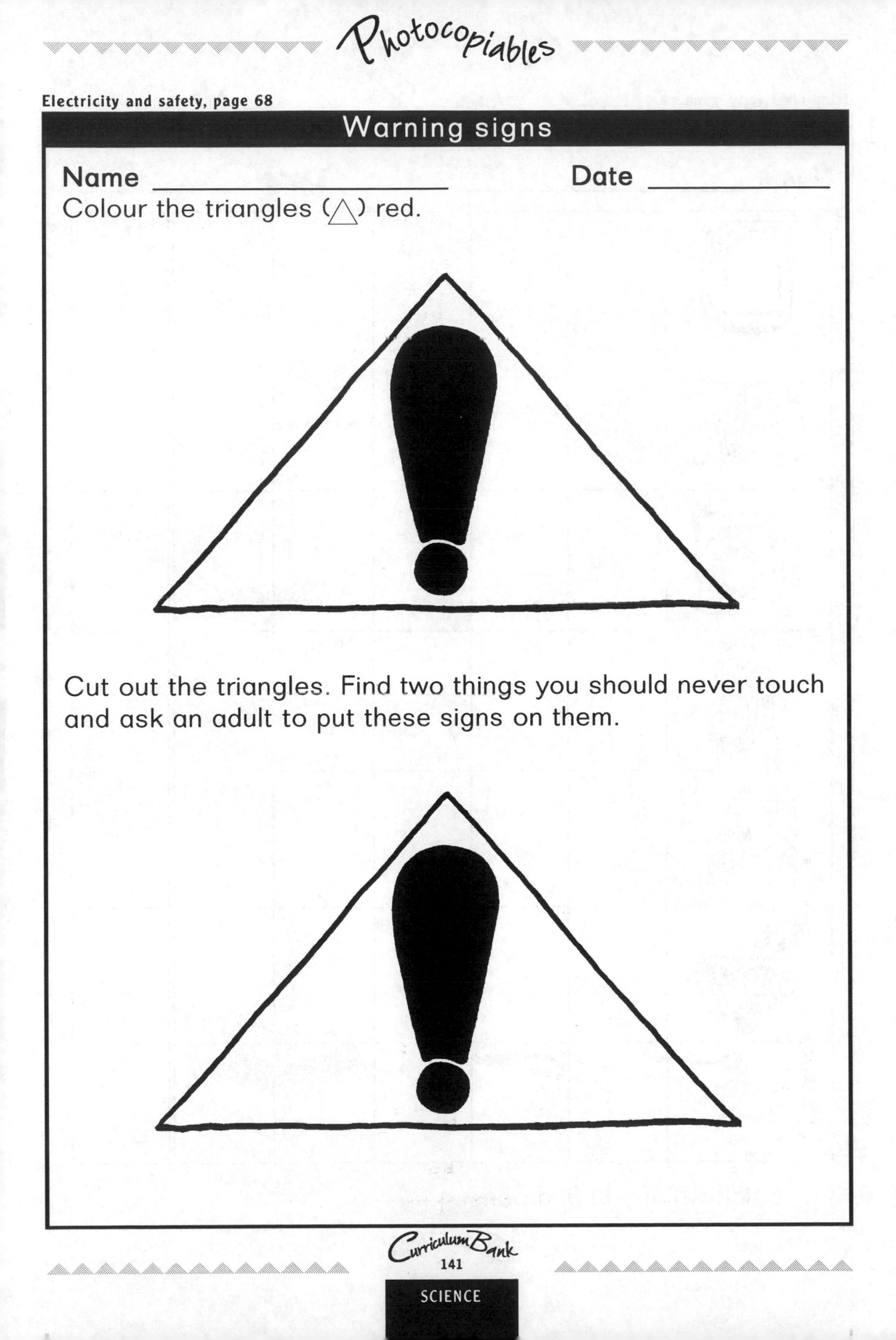

Cut out the triangles. Find two things you should never touch and ask an adult to put these signs on them.

Using electricity, page 69

Using electricity

Name _____   Date _____

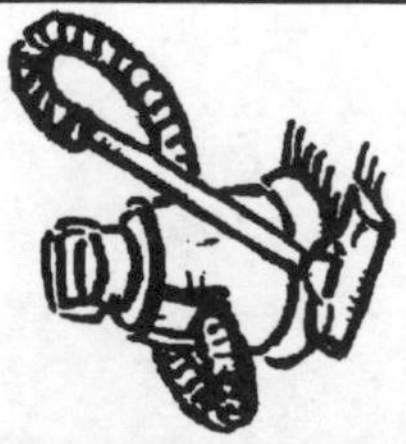

Which room?					How many?

Put a tick (✔) if you find one.

Making simple circuits, page 71

Lighting the bulb

Name _____   **Date** _____

Cut around the dotted lines.

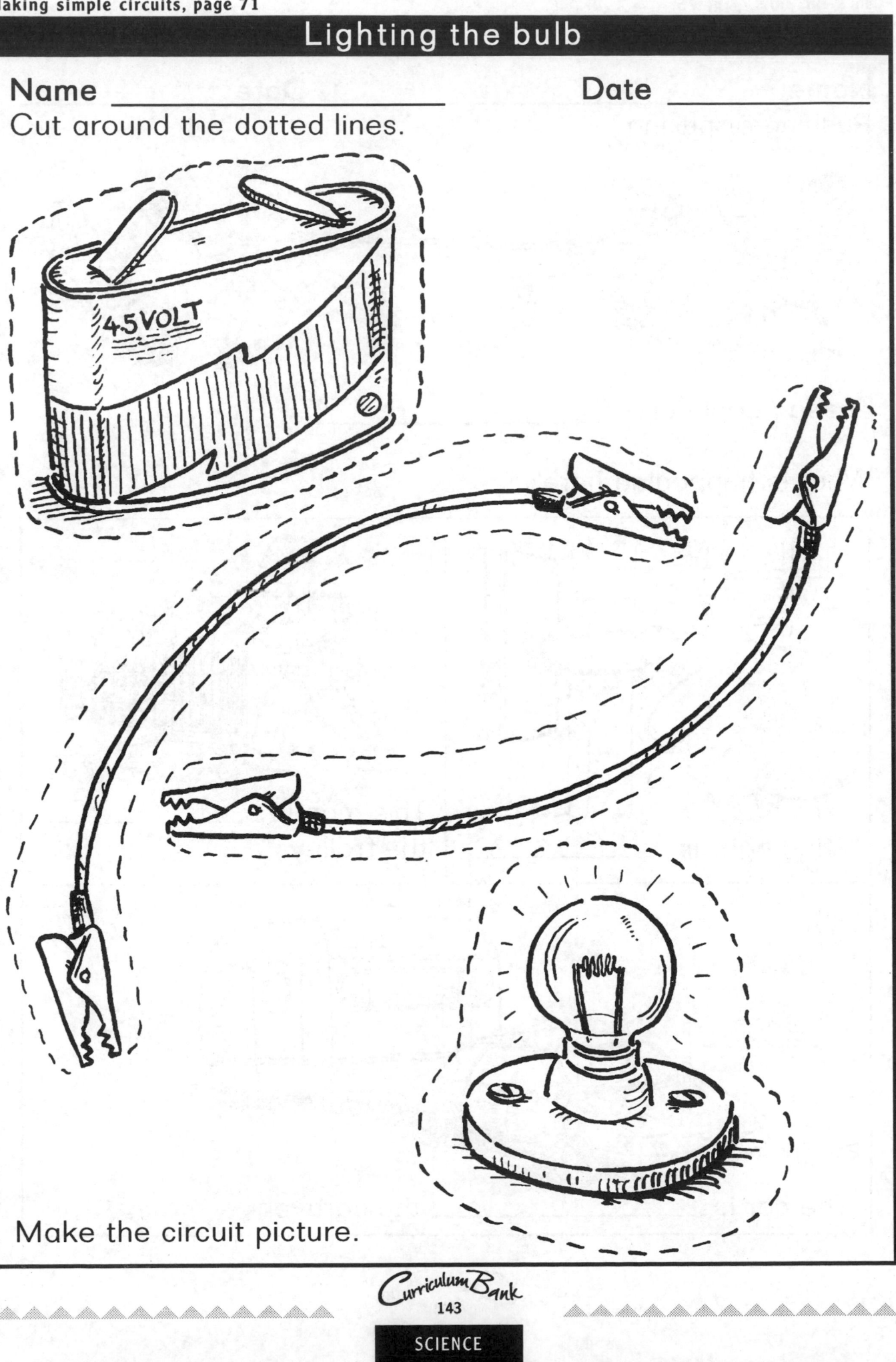

45 VOLT

Make the circuit picture.

Pushing or pulling

Name _____   **Date** _____

Pushing or pulling?

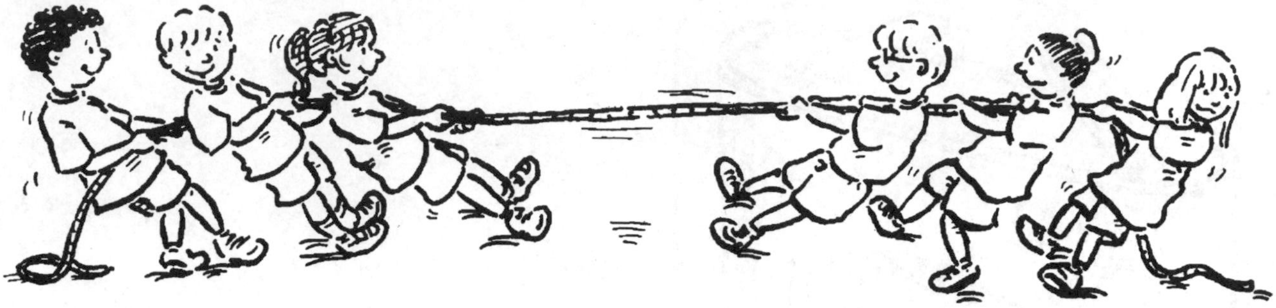

These people are _____

What is happening here?

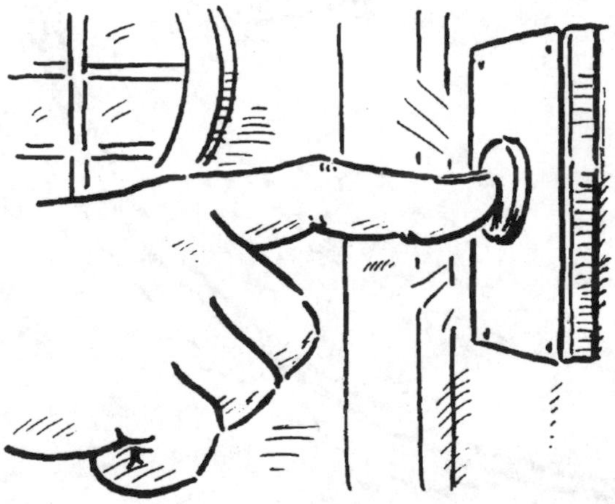

The finger is _____

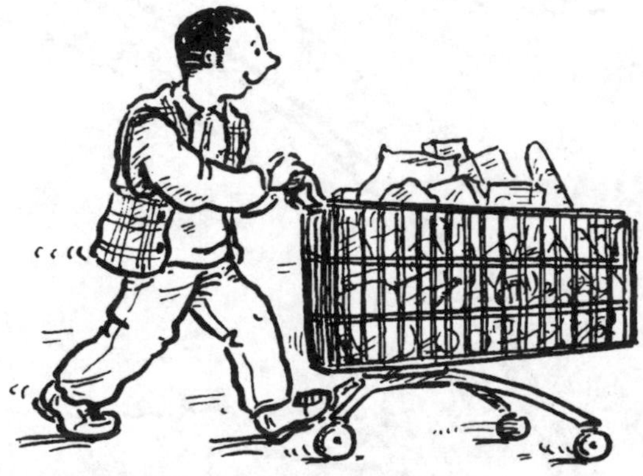

This man is _____ the trolley.

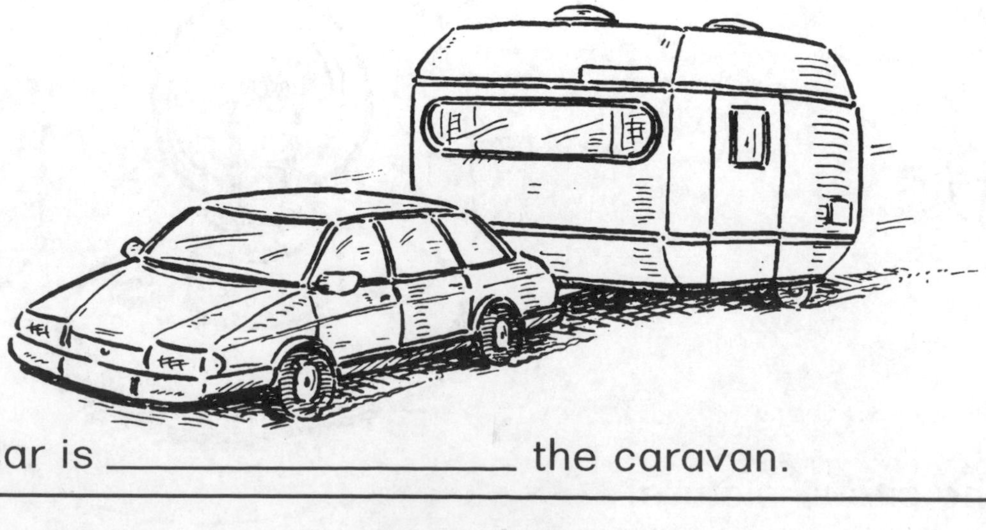

The car is _____ the caravan.

Light and reflection, page 79

Light sources

Name _____   **Date** _____

Colour the light sources.

Sounds good! page 83

We are the sound makers

We are the sound ma - kers, Clap your hands and stamp your feet

Co - py all the sounds we make, Add one to the beat.

First time – child one makes a sound 1
Second time – child two makes sound 1 and sound 2
Third time – child three makes sound 1, 2 and sound 3… and so on.

Verse
We are the sound makers,
Clap your hands and stamp your feet,
Copy all the sounds we make,
Add one to the beat.

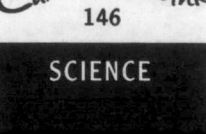

Birds, page 93

Bird cake recipe

½ kg lard or other animal fat
½ kg bird cake mixture or mixed seeds
additional quantities of stale cake, biscuits, left-over Christmas puddings and so on.

In a large saucepan heat the fat gently until completely melted, then remove the pan from the heat.
Add half the seeds and stir, then add the crumbled cake or biscuits and stir again.
Add more seeds until you have a firm, sticky mixture.
(The quantity of seeds used will vary according to your cake/biscuit mixture.)

Pierce holes in the base of plastic disposable drinking cups/empty yoghurt pots and insert a piece of string. Tie the string to a short length of stick (perhaps a matchstick with the head removed). Stand the pots on a foil-covered tray. Fill the pots with the mixture and allow this to set in the fridge.
Add a stick as a bird perch if you wish (see illustration).

Birds, page 93

Bird observation frequency chart

Name _____   **Date** _____

Bird/Feeder	Tally	Total

Seeds, page 96

Seed planting chart

Name _____   **Date** _____

I planted my seeds on

Type of seeds

Investigations, page 89

Investigating

Name _____   **Date** _____

1 What are you going to find out?

2 What did you do?

3 What happened?

4 What will you do next?

Plant and animal dominoes

needs some
water

I'm thirsty

needs a drink

I'm hungry

needs some
food

1
Start

lives in water

12
Finish

needs some
sun

Buttons, page 104

Buttons

Name _____   **Date** _____

What are your buttons made from?

10							
9							
8							
7							
6							
5							
4							
3							
2							
1							
0	metal	wood	rubber	plastic	fabric	paper	rock

1 Which material was used the most?

2 Which material was used the least?

3 How many buttons were covered in fabric?

Buttons, page 104

Material buttons

Name _____ **Date** _____

1 Without taking the fabric off, how can we find out if the material underneath is metal?

2 Why do you think no buttons are made from card, paper or rock?

3 Why do you think some buttons are made from metal?

4 Which material do you think makes the best button?

Why do you think that?

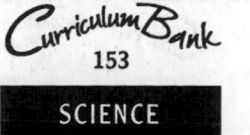

Bouncing balls, page 110

Which ball is best?

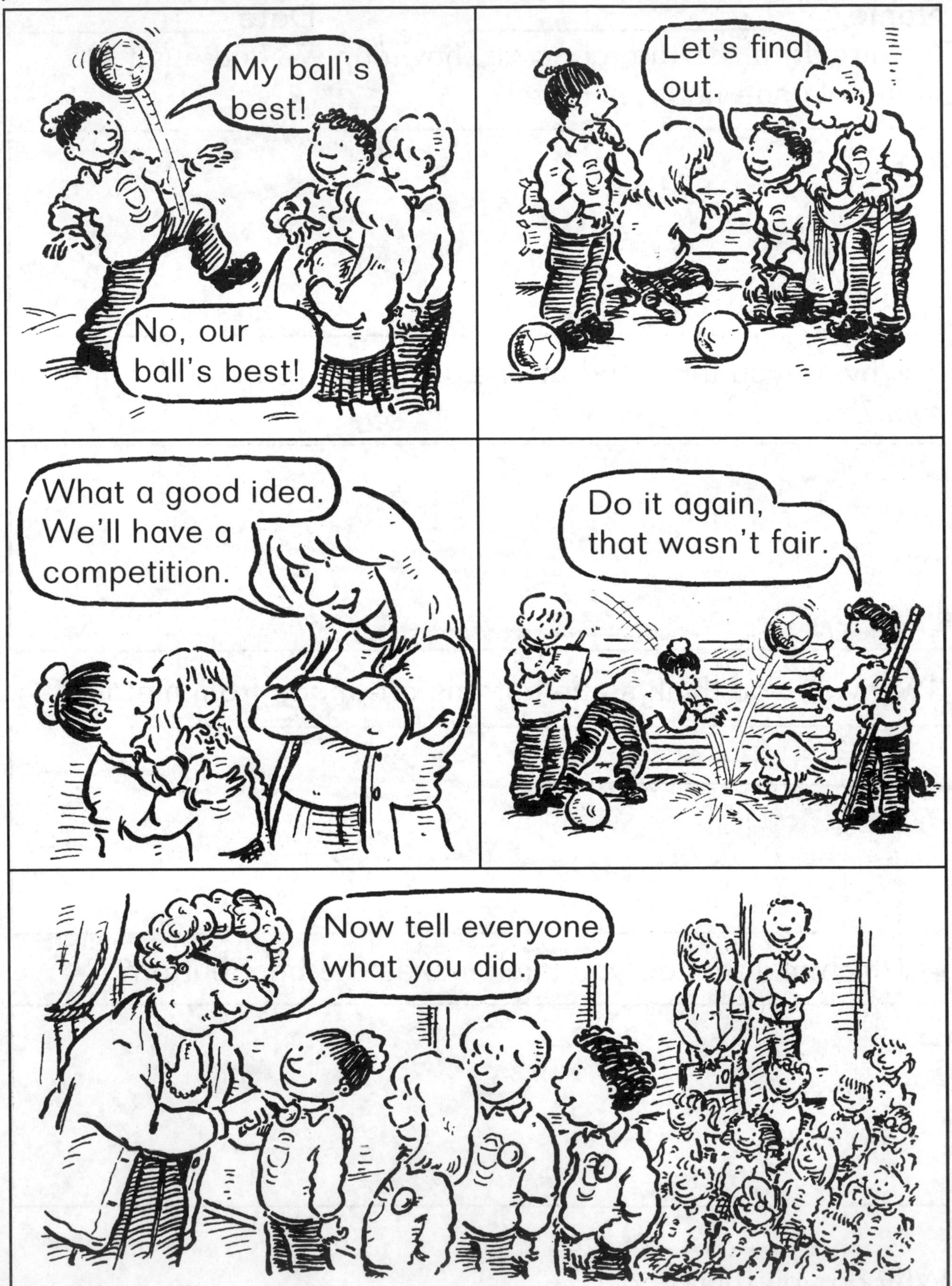

Bouncing balls, page 110

Bouncing balls

Name _____   **Date** _____

Show where each ball bounces.

Leaves, page 108

Skills recording sheet

Child's name	observing	sorting/ classifying	measuring/ comparing	raising questions	planning/ predicting	testing	drawing conclusions	recording	communicating findings

Let's twist again, page 60

Salt dough recipe

1 ½ kg plain flour
1 ½ pints water
500g salt
1 teaspoon cooking oil
food colouring

Mix the ingredients together in a large bowl until the right
consistency is obtained.
Store in a container with a tight-fitting lid
for up to two weeks.
Makes enough dough for
approximately four children.
Self-raising flour can be used
for a 'stretchier' dough.

INFORMATION TECHNOLOGY WITHIN SCIENCE AT KEY STAGE 1

Word processors

During Key Stage 1 pupils will be developing their confidence and competence to use the standard computer keyboard. They should be taught a range of basic keyboard and word-processing skills. These should include:

▲ an understanding of the layout of the keyboard and where the letter and number keys are found:

▲ how to get capital letters and characters found above the number keys using the *shift* key;

▲ how to use the *delete* key to erase words and letters;

▲ how to use the *cursor/arrow* keys, or mouse to position the cursor at the desired position;

▲ the use of more than a single finger/hand when typing, particularly as they become more proficient and know where letters are located;

▲ how to use the space bar; using their thumbs to press the space bar;

▲ how the word processor will 'wrap' the text around the end of the line so there is no need to press *return* at the end of each line;

▲ how to join text using the *delete* key;

▲ how to separate text or create new lines using the *return* key;

▲ how to move the cursor to a mistake and correct it, rather than deleting all the text back to a mistake, making the correction and then retyping the deleted text;

▲ how to print out their completed work, initially with support from the teacher, but eventually on their own.

Children will also need to save their work if they are unable to finish it in one session. They should be taught how to do this on to the hard or floppy disk so that eventually they can do it without teacher assistance. They will then need to be shown how to locate and retrieve their work at a later date.

Young children will take a long time to enter text at the keyboard so it is important to ensure that the writing tasks are kept short and that, where possible, there is other support available to teach and assist the child's development. If parents or other adults are available they can often be used in this way, provided they have the relevant skills, and know when to intervene. Alternatively they can be used for scribing for longer tasks, typing in the children's work and then going through it with them to edit and alter it.

For many of the writing tasks children can use the standard page format that is presented to them when the software is started. However for more complex tasks the teacher may wish to set up the page layout before the children start and save it, for example, as the menu layout. Children can then start with this basic menu layout and then begin to alter it if they need to.

Graphing software

A number of simple programs are available which let children enter a number of measurements or observations into tabular layout which is used by the software to draw a graph of the data provided. In simpler versions the graph is drawn as the information is entered. There is usually a facility to alter the type of graph drawn, with three main types, block graph, pie chart and line graph being the most common. Some software also enables children to sort the information into numerical or alphabetical order and then re-draw the graph.

Some programs allow children to use pictures to represent a single item, thus creating a pictogram which can later be redrawn as a block graph.

This type of software gives children a simple introduction to information handling, and can be useful in helping them gain a relationship between the size of block and the data entered; they can even be asked to predict how tall the next block will be before they enter the data. In the excitement of drawing the graph teachers should not forget that interpretation is an important aspect of the work.

Children should also discuss the benefits of drawing graphs in this way as against the traditional paper and pencil method. Ideas such as '*easier to correct mistakes*', '*can try out a different graph*', '*much quicker*', will show that children are beginning to understand the benefits of using the computer for such work.

Concept keyboards

Many schools have access to concept keyboards which can be linked to the word processor. These can be used with great effect for children at the end of Key Stage 1 when keyboard and writing skills are at an early stage of development. The small squares of the concept keyboard can be programmed so that when a child presses the word nail, or a picture of a nail, a nail will appear on the screen of the word processor.

Teachers can make their own overlays by using drawings or pictures taken from magazines or other educational resources. Words can also be included. It is also possible for children to use the computer keyboard to enter words which are not on the overlay. Although the overlays take a little time to set up initially they provide children with access to the computer. In many of the activities they can be used as a simple form of assessment, for example whether children can identify all of the magnetic materials in the list.

IT links

The information technology activities outlined in this book can be used to develop and assess children's IT capability as outlined in the National Curriculum. Types of software rather than names of specific programs have been mentioned to enable teachers to use the ideas regardless of which computer they are using. Teachers may still want to include specific software which runs on their computer and which addresses the content and understanding of the subject being taught. However they should be aware that although such software may assist pupils in their learning of science, it may add little to the development of their pupils' IT capability.

AREA OF IT	TYPE OF SOFTWARE	ACTIVITIES (page nos.)		
		CHAPTER 1	CHAPTER 2	CHAPTER 3
Communicating information	Word processor	16, 18, 21, 26, 27, 33, 42	48, 50, 51, 57, 65	75, 79,
Communicating information	Concept keyboard		48, 50, 51, 57, 65	75, 79,
Communicating information	Art/graphics	34, 37		
Information handling	Database	22		83
Information handling	Graphing software	20, 22, 29, 30, 33, 42	53	69, 77, 81
Information handling	Branching database	32, 45		
Information handling	CD-ROM	39, 41		83
Control	Roamer/Turtle			72, 74
Control	Tape recorders	18, 39		85

SOFTWARE TYPE	BBC/MASTER	RISCOS	NIMBUS/186	WINDOWS	MACINTOSH
Word processor	Stylus Folio Prompt/Writer	Phases Pendown Desk Top Folio	All Write Write On	My Word Kid Works 2 Creative Writer	Kid Works 2 Easy Works Creative Writer
Framework		My World		My World	
Art package	Picture Builder	1st Paint Kid Pix Splash	Picture Builder	Colour Magic Kid Pix 2	Kid Pix 2
Database	Our Facts Grass Pigeonhole Datashow	DataSweet Find IT	Our Facts Datashow	Sparks Claris Works Information Workshop	Claris Works Easy Works
Branching database	Branch	Retreeval	Branch		
Graphing software	Datashow	Pictogram Picture Point DataSweet	Datagraph	Datagraph Easy Works	Easy Works
Control	Roamer, PIPP, Turtle				

	ENGLISH	MATHS	HISTORY	GEOGRAPHY	D&T	IT	ART	MUSIC	RE	PE
SENSES		Shape.			Textiles: fabric pictures with different feeling surfaces.		Collage.	Listening: high/low; long/short; loud/soft.	Keeping ourselves and feelings safe.	Dance: to explore moods and feelings through dance.
OURSELVES	Descriptive writing.	Measuring; collecting, recording and interpreting data.	Our Family: finding out about the past, identifying how life is different today.	Where we live; road safety.		Drawing graphs: entering and storing information.	Portraits.	Playground games and rhymes.	Families and friends.	Develop control, coordination, and balance in travelling; running and chasing games.
PLANTS	'Jack and the Beanstalk' and associated activities.	Measuring; collecting, recording and interpreting data.		The School Environment; growing plants in the school environment.	Food: what vegetables and fruits do we eat? Making salads and soups.	Graphics: using *Paint* to make a picture of a garden.	Landscapes.		Caring for the environment.	Growing: developing sequences, change in shape and levels.
ANIMALS	Animal stories to write and listen to.		Dinosaurs.	The School Environment.		Word processing: animal stories.	Painting.	Performing: animal songs.	Caring for animals.	Movement: developing sequences, change in travelling, jumping, turning and gestures.
GROUPING MATERIALS	Creative writing: invitations to Teddy Bears' Picnic.	Sorting information.		House and Homes: use of materials in the home and local environment.	Food: organising picnic; making and presenting food.	Drawing graphs. Entering and storing information.	Collage. Sculpture. Painting with threads.	Investigating sounds of different materials.	Churches.	Contrasts of speed, shape, direction and level.
CHANGING MATERIALS			Houses and Homes: how have materials changed in construction?				Pottery; sculpture.		Festivals: Hanukkah, Diwali, Christmas.	Ways of sending and receiving; games equipment.
MOVEMENT		Describing positions; studying angles, right angles, half and quarter turns.	Transport	Journeys: routes, pathways, coordinates; road safety; transport.	Construction: making moving vehicles and toys.	Control: writing pathways for *Pip and Roamer.*				Travelling: using hands and feet, on floor and using apparatus.
LIGHT							Colour mixing.			
SOUND	Writing sound poems and stories.				Construction: making musical instruments and accompaniments.	Using a tape recorder to record poems and accompaniments.		Composing simple sound effects and accompaniments for poems.	Celebration.	Dance: exploring contrasts of rhythm and speed.